Revision notes

Credit Level

Maths
revision notes

✕ Ken Nisbet ✕

Text © 2003 Ken Nisbet
Design and layout © 2003 Leckie & Leckie
Cover image ©1999 Nick Koudis/PhotoDisc, Inc

1st Edition (reprinted 2005)

ISBN 1-84372-079-5

Published by
Leckie & Leckie Ltd, 3rd floor, 4 Queen Street, Edinburgh, EH2 1JF
Tel: 0131 220 6831 Fax: 0131 225 9987
enquiries@leckieandleckie.co.uk   www.leckieandleckie.co.uk

Special thanks to
Julie Barclay (design), David Collins (proofreading), Merlyn Gudgeon (illustration),
Caleb Rutherford (cover design), Phoenix Design (layout design), Robin Waterson (editing)

A CIP Catalogue record for this book is available from the British Library.

Leckie & Leckie Ltd is a division of Granada Learning Limited.

Contents

These Course Notes will prepare you for the SQA Mathematics Standard Grade Credit Level Exam. They have been written to cover the Credit Level content as laid down in the *Standard Grade Arrangements in Mathematics* document published by the Scottish Qualifications Authority in April 2000. Some General Level content appears where this is a necessary and natural introduction to the Credit Level topic. However these notes are not appropriate if you are preparing for the General Level Exam. We would recommend Leckie & Leckie's *Standard Grade Maths Revision Notes* for this purpose.

The current structure of the Credit Exam is as follows:

Paper 1 (Non-Calculator)	Time: 55 min
Paper 2 (Calculator allowed)	Time: 80 min

The following Formulae List is given to you in the exam:

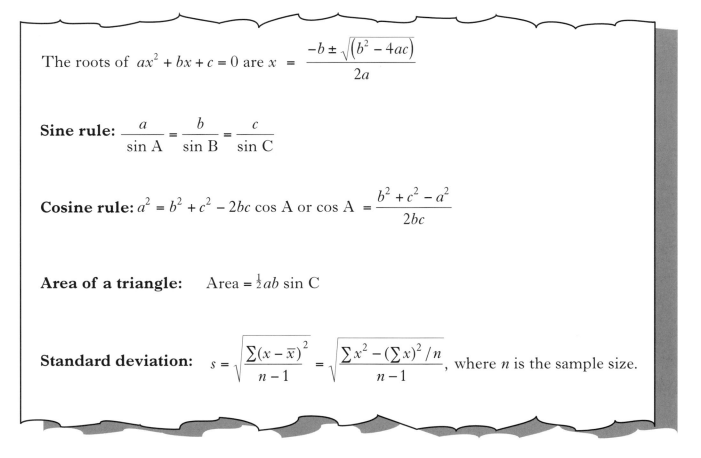

The roots of $ax^2 + bx + c = 0$ are $x = \dfrac{-b \pm \sqrt{(b^2 - 4ac)}}{2a}$

Sine rule: $\dfrac{a}{\sin A} = \dfrac{b}{\sin B} = \dfrac{c}{\sin C}$

Cosine rule: $a^2 = b^2 + c^2 - 2bc \cos A$ or $\cos A = \dfrac{b^2 + c^2 - a^2}{2bc}$

Area of a triangle: $\text{Area} = \tfrac{1}{2}ab \sin C$

Standard deviation: $s = \sqrt{\dfrac{\sum(x - \bar{x})^2}{n - 1}} = \sqrt{\dfrac{\sum x^2 - (\sum x)^2 / n}{n - 1}}$, where n is the sample size.

In these notes key points have been emphasised, vital facts have been clearly summarised and all necessary techniques illustrated with a host of worked examples. Calculator hints are indicated by ⌨. At all times the language used and the style of explanation are such that you can easily relate to the ideas and thus gain necessary understanding. A comprehensive index has been provided for quick access to particular topics, terms and ideas.

Types of Numbers

You will need to recognise the following types of numbers:

Whole Numbers	0, 1, 2, 3, 4, ...
Integers	..., −3, −2, −1, 0, 1, 2, 3, ...

Negative Integers   Positive Integers

Rational Numbers (Fractions)   These are numbers that can be written as a 'ratio' of two integers, e.g. $\frac{3}{5}$, $-3 = \frac{-3}{1}$, $2{\cdot}75 = 2\frac{3}{4} = \frac{11}{4}$ etc.

Note Rational Numbers such as 2·75 are called decimal fractions.

Real Numbers   These are numbers that can be represented by all the points on the Real Number Line. Here are examples:

$$-3 \qquad -\sqrt{3} \qquad -0{\cdot}9 \qquad 0 \qquad \tfrac{1}{3} \qquad \sqrt{2} \qquad 2 \qquad \pi$$

Note Real Numbers that are not Rational are called Irrational, e.g. $\sqrt{2}$ and π.

Decimal Places

Decimal places are counted immediately to the right of the decimal point.

$$0 \cdot 1\ 2\ 3$$

1st decimal place   2nd decimal place   3rd decimal place

Example 1.1.1

To how many decimal places are these measurements written?

(a) 8·2 m   (b) 0·03 kg   (c) 14·803 s

Solution
(a) 1 decimal place (d. p.)
(b) 2 d. p.
(c) 3 d. p.

Significant Figures

The measurements

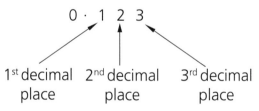

and   0·0 0 4 0 5 0 km
and   4·0 5 0 m
and   4 0 5·0 cm   are the same.

Leading zeros are **not** significant.   Trailing zeros after the decimal point **are** significant.

Significant figures are counted immediately to the right of any leading zeros:

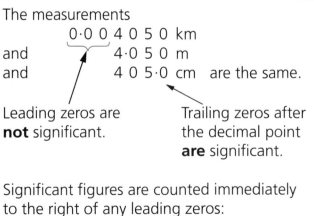

0·0 0 4 0 5 0

1st   2nd   3rd   4th   significant figure

Example 1.1.2

How many significant figures do the following measurements have?

(a) 26·5 cm   (b) 20·04 kg
(c) 0·020 m²   (d) 260 tonnes

Solution
(a) 3 significant figures (s. f.)
(b) 4 s. f.
(c) 2 s. f.
(d) 2 s. f. (if it is to the nearest 10 tonnes)
    or
    3 s. f. (if it is to the nearest 1 tonne)

1.1 Numbers and Accuracy

Rounding Measurements

The Rounding Rules ···$\boxed{7}\boxed{8}\boxed{3}\boxed{4}\boxed{7}\boxed{2}$···

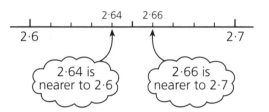

Example 1.1.

Round each of these
(i) 3 significant figures

(a) 24·66 cm (b) 0·2495 g

Solution

(a) (i) 24·66 ÷ 24·7 cm (to 3 s. f.)

(ii) 24·66 ÷ 20 cm (to 1 s. f.)

(b) (i) 0·2495 ÷ 0·250 g (to 3 s. f.)

(ii) 0·2495 ÷ 0·2 g (to 1 s. f.)

Advice on Rounding

It is useful to draw number lines:

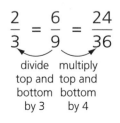

Never round the values in a calculation until the final answer is obtained. Calculating with rounded numbers leads to inaccurate results.

Do not leave more significant figures in the answer to a calculation than there were in the measurements you used for the calculation. (Final accuracy depends on initial accuracy!)

1.2 Calculations with Fractions

Equivalent Fractions

Identical factors in the numerator (top number) and denominator (bottom number) may be cancelled. In other words the numerator and denominator may be divided by the same number without altering the value of the fraction.

Similarly the numerator and denominator may be multiplied by the same number without altering the value of the fraction:

$$\frac{2}{3} = \frac{6}{9} = \frac{24}{36}$$

divide top and bottom by 3 multiply top and bottom by 4

Example 1.2.1

Simplify $\frac{18}{42}$

Solution

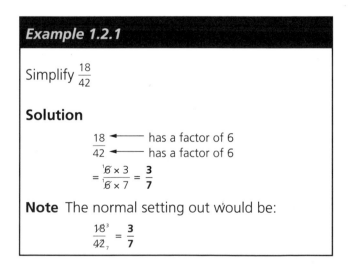

$\dfrac{18}{42}$ ← has a factor of 6
← has a factor of 6

$= \dfrac{\cancel{6} \times 3}{\cancel{6} \times 7} = \dfrac{3}{7}$

Note The normal setting out would be:

$\dfrac{\cancel{18}^{3}}{\cancel{42}_{7}} = \dfrac{3}{7}$

...r such as $3\frac{2}{5}$ is called a **mixed number**. It may be written as a 'top-heavy' fraction as follows:

$$3\frac{2}{5} = 3 + \frac{2}{5} = \frac{15}{5} + \frac{2}{5} = \frac{17}{5}$$

Each of these 3 wholes may be
changed to 5 lots of $\frac{1}{5}$
giving 15 lots of $\frac{1}{5}$ i.e. $\frac{15}{5}$

15 lots
of $\frac{1}{5}$

2 lots
of $\frac{1}{5}$

17 lots
of $\frac{1}{5}$

Note The 'no understanding method' is: $3\frac{2}{5} = \frac{17}{5}$ by calculating $5 \times 3 + 2$.

A fraction such as $\frac{19}{3}$ which is 'top-heavy' may be written as a mixed number as follows:

$$\frac{19}{3} = \frac{18}{3} + \frac{1}{3} = 6 + \frac{1}{3} = 6\frac{1}{3}$$

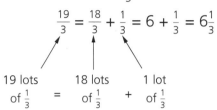

19 lots
of $\frac{1}{3}$

=

18 lots
of $\frac{1}{3}$

+

1 lot
of $\frac{1}{3}$

Note: The calculation here is 3 into 19 gives 6 times, remainder 1, so $\frac{19}{3} = 6\frac{1}{3}$.

Multiplying Fractions

The basic rule is:

e.g. $\frac{2}{3} \times \frac{5}{7}$ ———— Multiply the two numerators.
———— Multiply the two denominators.

$= \frac{2 \times 5}{3 \times 7} = \frac{10}{21}$

If there are identical factors in a numerator and a denominator it is wise to cancel this factor before multiplying.

Dividing Fractions

After any mixed numbers are changed to 'top-heavy' fractions you should rewrite the division as a 'double-decker' fraction. Examples of 'double-deckers' include:

$\frac{2/5}{8}, \frac{2}{1/3}$ and $\frac{23/7}{46/21}$

The numerator (top number) and the denominator (bottom number) may now be multiplied by the same number. The number you multiply by is chosen so that any cancelling reduces the 'double-decker' to a 'single decker'. You can see this in action in Example 1.2.3 opposite.

Example 1.2.2

Evaluate $2\frac{2}{3} \times 3\frac{3}{4}$

Solution $2\frac{2}{3} \times 3\frac{3}{4}$ Change these to 'top-heavy' fractions.

$= \frac{8}{3} \times \frac{15}{4}$ Now cancel the factor 3 and also the factor 4.

$= \frac{\overset{2}{\cancel{8}}}{\cancel{3}_{1}} \times \frac{\overset{5}{\cancel{15}}}{\cancel{4}_{1}} = \frac{2 \times 5}{1 \times 1} = \frac{10}{1} = \mathbf{10}$

Example 1.2.3

Evaluate (a) $2 \div \frac{1}{3}$ (b) $\frac{2}{5} \div 8$ (c) $3\frac{2}{7} \div 2\frac{4}{21}$

Solution

(a) $\frac{2}{\frac{1}{3}}$ It is the 'divide by 3' that makes this a 'double-decker' so multiply top and bottom by 3 to cancel it.

$\frac{2 \times 3}{\frac{1}{3} \times 3} = \frac{6}{1} = \mathbf{6}$

(b) $\frac{\frac{2}{5}}{8}$ This time you need to cancel the 'divide by 5' so multiply top and bottom by 5.

$= \frac{\frac{2}{5} \times 5}{8 \times 5} = \frac{\overset{1}{\cancel{2}}}{\cancel{40}_{20}} = \frac{1}{\mathbf{20}}$

(c) $3\frac{2}{7} \div 2\frac{4}{21} = \frac{23}{7} \div \frac{46}{21} = \frac{\frac{23}{7}}{\frac{46}{21}}$ Multiply top and bottom by 21.

$= \frac{\frac{23}{7} \times \overset{3}{\cancel{21}}}{\frac{46}{\cancel{21}_{1}} \times 21} = \frac{\overset{1}{\cancel{23}} \times 3}{\cancel{46}_{2} \times 1} = \frac{1 \times 3}{2 \times 1} = \frac{3}{2} = \mathbf{1\frac{1}{2}}$

Adding and Subtracting Fractions

The aim is to get the two denominators (bottom numbers) the same.

For example: $\frac{2}{3} + \frac{4}{5}$

2 lots of $\frac{1}{3}$ 4 lots of $\frac{1}{5}$

Thirds and fifths are different so...

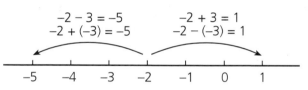

$\frac{2}{3} + \frac{4}{5} = \frac{2 \times 5}{3 \times 5} + \frac{4 \times 3}{5 \times 3} = \frac{10}{15} + \frac{12}{15} = \frac{22}{15}$

10 lots of $\frac{1}{15}$ + 12 lots of $\frac{1}{15}$ = 22 lots of $\frac{1}{15}$

Example 1.2.4

Evaluate $2\frac{1}{3} + 1\frac{1}{4} - 1\frac{5}{6}$

Solution

$2\frac{1}{3} + 1\frac{1}{4} - 1\frac{5}{6}$ Change these to 'top-heavy' fractions.

$= \frac{7}{3} + \frac{5}{4} - \frac{11}{6}$ Change $\frac{1}{3}, \frac{1}{4}$ and $\frac{1}{6}$ to $\frac{1}{12}$.

$= \frac{7 \times 4}{3 \times 4} + \frac{5 \times 3}{4 \times 3} - \frac{11 \times 2}{6 \times 2}$

$= \frac{28}{12} + \frac{15}{12} - \frac{22}{12}$ There are 28 + 15 − 22 lots of $\frac{1}{12}$ here.

$= \frac{28 + 15 - 22}{12} = \frac{21^{7}}{12_{4}} = \frac{7}{4} = \mathbf{1\frac{3}{4}}$

1.3 Calculations with Integers

Adding and Subtracting Integers

Use the number line:

$-2 - 3 = -5$ $-2 + 3 = 1$
$-2 + (-3) = -5$ $-2 - (-3) = 1$

$\begin{array}{ccccccc} -5 & -4 & -3 & -2 & -1 & 0 & 1 \end{array}$

Notice that:
Adding a negative is the same as subtracting
so +(−3) gives −3

Subtracting a negative is the same as adding
so −(−3) gives +3

Example 1.3.1

Calculate the next three terms in the sequence 5, −4, 1, ... where the rule is 'add the two previous terms to get the next term'

Solution

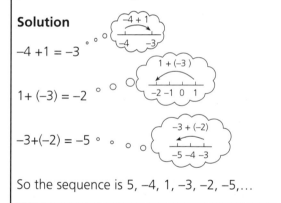

$-4 + 1 = -3$

$1 + (-3) = -2$

$-3 + (-2) = -5$

So the sequence is 5, −4, 1, −3, −2, −5,...

Multiplying and Dividing Integers

Use the rules:
positive × positive
negative × negative } gives positive

negative × positive
positive × negative } gives negative

Exactly the same rules apply to dividing two integers.

Example 1.3.2

Calculate (a) $(-2)^4$ (b) $\frac{-3 + (-5) \times 3}{-2 \times 3}$

Solution

(a) $(-2)^4 = -2 \times (-2) \times (-2) \times (-2)$
$= -2 \times (-2) \times 4$ (since neg × neg is pos)
$= -2 \times (-8)$ (since neg × pos is neg)
$= \mathbf{16}$ (again since neg × neg is pos)

(b) $\frac{-3 + (-5) \times 3}{-2 \times 3} = \frac{-3 + (-15)}{-6} = \frac{-18}{-6} = \mathbf{3}$
(neg ÷ neg is pos)

Integral Indices

A positive integer index counts the repeated factor in a multiplication:

e.g. $2^5 = 2 \times 2 \times 2 \times 2 \times 2$

Here there are five factors of 2 in the multiplication

An index of zero gives an answer of 1:

e.g. $5^0 = 1$, $8^0 = 1$, $(\frac{1}{2})^0 = 1$

A negative index is rewritten as 1 divided by the same thing to the positive index:

e.g. $3^{-2} = \frac{1}{3^2}$

Example 1.4.1

Evaluate: (a) $2^3 \times 3^2$ (b) $5^2 \times 3^{-4}$

Solution:

(a) $2^3 \times 3^2 = \underset{(2\times2\times2)}{8} \times \underset{(3\times3)}{9} = 72$

(b) $5^2 \times 3^{-4} = 5^2 \times \frac{1}{3^4} = \underset{(5\times5)}{25} \times \underset{(3\times3\times3\times3)}{\frac{1}{81}} = \frac{25}{81}$

Fractional Indices

For a fractional index the top number gives the power and the bottom number gives the type of root.

e.g. $16^{\frac{3}{2}}$ — power 3 (cubed), square root

$8^{\frac{2}{3}}$ — power 2 (squared), cube root

$= (\sqrt{16})^3 = 4^3 = 64$ $= (\sqrt[3]{8})^2 = 2^2 = 4$

Note: **Cube Roots** $\sqrt[3]{8} = 2$ since $2^3 = 8$

$\sqrt[3]{27} = 3$ since $3^3 = 27$

$\sqrt[3]{64} = 4$ since $4^3 = 64$ etc

4th Roots $\sqrt[4]{16} = 2$ since $2^4 = 16$

$\sqrt[4]{81} = 3$ since $3^4 = 81$ etc

Example 1.4.2

Evaluate $16^{\frac{3}{4}} \times 8^{\frac{-4}{3}}$

Solution

$16^{\frac{3}{4}} \times 8^{\frac{-4}{3}} = 16^{\frac{3}{4}} \times \frac{1}{8^{\frac{4}{3}}} = \frac{16^{\frac{3}{4}}}{8^{\frac{4}{3}}}$

$= \frac{(\sqrt[4]{16})^3}{(\sqrt[3]{8})^4} = \frac{2^3}{2^4} = \frac{8}{16} = \frac{1}{2}$

Scientific Notation

A number written in the form $a \times 10^n$ where $1 \le a < 10$ and n is an integer is written in **scientific notation** or **standard form**. Examples include: $2{\cdot}6 \times 10^3 = 2600$ and $9{\cdot}82 \times 10^{-2} = 0{\cdot}0982$

Notice that the index indicates where the decimal point is placed.
So $\times 10^3$: move the point 3 places to the right $\times 10^{-2}$: move the point 2 places to the left.

Notice that the first number, e.g. $2{\cdot}6$ or $9{\cdot}82$, must always lie between 1 or 10 (or be equal to 1).

Calculations in Scientific Notation

When the powers of 10 are multiplied **add** the indices. When the powers of 10 are divided **subtract** the indices. Always check that the first number is between 1 and 10. If it is not, then rewrite it in scientific notation.

Note

Numbers in Scientific Notation may be entered directly into your calculator. This is done using the special $\boxed{\text{EXP}}$ or $\boxed{\text{EE}}$ key.
For example to enter $4{\cdot}8 \times 10^3$ you press:
$\boxed{4} \boxed{\cdot} \boxed{8} \boxed{\text{EXP}} \boxed{3}$
See your calculator manual for more details.

Example 1.4.3

Calculate   (a) $(2{\cdot}3 \times 10^{-2}) \times (5 \times 10^5)$

(b) $\frac{8 \times 10^2}{2 \times 10^{-3}}$

giving your answers in scientific notation

Solution (a) $2{\cdot}3 \times 10^{-2} \times 5 \times 10^5$

$= 2{\cdot}3 \times 5 \times 10^{-2} \times 10^5 = 11{\cdot}5 \times 10^3$

add the indices   not between
$-2 + 5 = 3$ 1 and 10

$= 1{\cdot}15 \times 10^1 \times 10^3 = \mathbf{1{\cdot}15 \times 10^4}$

(b) $\frac{8 \times 10^2}{2 \times 10^{-3}} = \frac{8}{2} \times \frac{10^2}{10^{-3}} = 4 \times 10^{2-(-3)} = \mathbf{4 \times 10^5}$

Basic Percentage Calculations

Type 1 Finding a % of a quantity

step 1 Divide the percentage number by 100.

step 2 Multiply by the quantity.

Example 1.5.1

VAT (Value Added Tax) is charged at 17·5%. Find, to the nearest penny, the VAT added to a bill of £525.

Solution

17·5% of £525 = $\frac{17 \cdot 5}{100}$ × 525

(Divide by 100, multiply by 525.)

= 91·875

The VAT is **£91·88** (to nearest penny).

Type 2 Expressing one quantity as a % of another quantity

step 1 Divide the 1st quantity by the 2nd quantity.

step 2 Multiply by 100% (to change the fraction to a percentage).

Example 1.5.2

A CD is sold at £14 for a profit of £4. Express this profit as a % of the buying price (i.e. the price the shop paid for the CD).

Solution

Profit £4 with a buying price of £10.

% Profit = $\frac{4}{10}$ × 100%

= **40%**

Using a Multiplier

Appreciation is when a value increases.

To increase £230, for example, by 15%:

115% = $\frac{115}{100}$ = 1·15 (the multiplier)

The answer is given by:
£230 × 1·15 = £264·50

Check this on your calculator.

Example 1.5.3

A house bought for £90 000 appreciates in value by 5% each year. What is it worth after 3 years? (Give your answer to the nearest £1000.)

Solution

100% + 5% = 105% = $\frac{105}{100}$ = 1·05

(This is the multiplier.)

Value at start = £90 000
After 1 year: £90 000 × 1·05 = £94 500
After 2 years: £94 500 × 1·05 = £99 225
After 3 years: £99 225 × 1·05 = £104 186·25

Final value = **£104 000** (to the nearest £1000)

Depreciation is when a value decreases.

To decrease £230, for example, by 15%:

85% = $\frac{85}{100}$ = 0·85 (the multiplier)

The answer is given by:
£230 × 0·85 = £195·50

Example 1.5.4

Company shares worth £1200 depreciate in value over a month by 12% but then appreciate by 13% over the next month. Are they now worth more or less than before?

Solution

After 1st month: £1200 × 0·88 = £1056
(100% − 12% = 88% = 0·88 is the multiplier.)

After 2nd month: £1056 × 1·13 = £1193·28
(100% + 13% = 113% = 1·13 is the multiplier.)

So they are worth **£6·72 less**.

Compound Interest

Money which is invested (called the **principal**) usually grows in value. This extra value is called **interest**.

Interest is calculated as a percentage of the principal invested. The percentage used for this calculation is called the **rate of interest**.

The letters p.a. stand for 'per annum' and mean that the interest is calculated for 1 complete year.

When the interest is not withdrawn but is added to the investment, it will also start to gain interest. This is called **compound interest**.

Further Percentage Calculations

Type 3 Given the final amount after a % increase or decrease, finding the original amount before the change

step 1 For an increase add the % to 100. For a decrease subtract the % from 100.

step 2 Divide the final amount by the answer to step 1. (This calculates 1% of the amount.)

step 3 Multiply by 100. (This calculates 100% of the original amount.)

Inflation

Over time, prices tend to increase. The **inflation rate** measures this increase. For example, during 2000 in the UK, the annual inflation rate was 3%.

Ratio

The ratio m:n can be thought of as a sharing of 'lots'. A total of m+n 'lots' are to be shared out as follows: m 'lots' to n 'lots'. For example, if £15 is to be shared between two people in the ratio 2:3, then there are 5 'lots' in total. Each 'lot' is worth $\frac{1}{5}$ of £15 = £3. So 2 'lots' make £6 and 3 'lots' make £9.

Example 1.5.5

Calculate the compound interest and the final amount for an investment of £950 for 2 years at 6% p.a.

Solution

$100\% + 6\% = 106\% = \frac{106}{100} = 1\cdot06$

(This is the multiplier.)

1st year: Amount = £950 × 1·06 = £1007
2nd year: Amount = £1007 × 1·06 = £1067·42
i.e. Final Amount = **£1067·42**
Compound interest = £1067·42 − £950
= **£117·42**

Example 1.5.6

After a 15% sales reduction, a TV costs £306. What was its original price?

Solution

$100\% - 15\% = 85\%$ ⟷ £306
So 1% ⟷ $£\frac{306}{85}$
So 100% ⟷ $£\frac{306}{85} \times 100$
= £360

Original price was **£360**.

Example 1.5.7

By how much should a weekly pay packet of £230 increase to keep in line with an inflation rate of 4·2% over a year?

Solution

4·2% of £230 = $\frac{4\cdot2}{100} \times 230$ = £9·66

A **£9·66** increase would be needed.

Example 1.5.8

Ian and Rob share a flat and agree to divide their bills for telephone (£83·76) and gas (£121·84) in the ratio 7:3. How much does each pay?

Solution: For 7:3 there are 10 'lots'. The total bill is £83·76 + £121·84 = £205·60. $\frac{1}{10}$ of £205·60 = £20·56. This is 1 'lot'.

So Ian pays 7 'lots': 7 × £20·56 = **£143·92**; and Rob pays 3 'lots': 3 × £20·56 = **£61·68**.

Reminders

Area is measured in square units. A square centimetre is shown on the right.

1 cm² : 1 cm

1 cm

Rectangle

b

l

$A = l \times b$

Triangle

h

b

$A = \frac{1}{2}b \times h$

Circle

r

$A = \pi r^2$

Volume is measured in cube units. A centimetre cube is shown on the right.

1 cm³ : 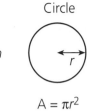 1 cm

1 cm

1 cm

It has different names:

      1 cubic centimetre (1 cc)

or   1 millilitre (1 ml)

so   1000 cm³ = 1 litre.

Example 2.1.1

Find the area of a circle with diameter 13 cm.

Solution

Use $A = \pi r^2$ with $r = 6{\cdot}5$ cm

                   (half the diameter)

So $A = \pi \times 6{\cdot}5^2$

       $= 132{\cdot}73 \ldots$

       $\doteqdot$ **132·7 cm²** (to 1 d. p.)

Spheres

The volume, V unit³, of a sphere with radius r units is given by:

$$V = \tfrac{4}{3}\pi r^3$$

Use the following key sequence:

$\boxed{4}\ \boxed{\div}\ \boxed{3}\ \boxed{\times}\ \boxed{\pi}\ \boxed{\times}$ ...(enter radius)... $\boxed{y^x}\ \boxed{3}\ \boxed{=}$

               or↗ ↖or

             $\boxed{x^y}$ $\boxed{\wedge}$

Half a sphere is called a **hemisphere**.

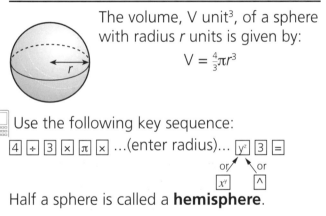

To find its volume, calculate the volume of the whole sphere then divide by 2.

(Remember that if you are given the diameter then divide it by 2 to get the radius, before using the volume formula).

Example 2.1.2

Find the volume of a sphere with diameter 14 cm. (Give your answer to 3 significant figures.)

Solution

Use $V = \tfrac{4}{3}\pi r^3$ with $r = 7$ cm

                 (half the diameter)

So $V = \tfrac{4}{3} \times \pi \times 7^3$

       $= 1436{\cdot}75 \ldots$

       $\doteqdot$ **1440 cm³** (to 3 s. f.)

Cones

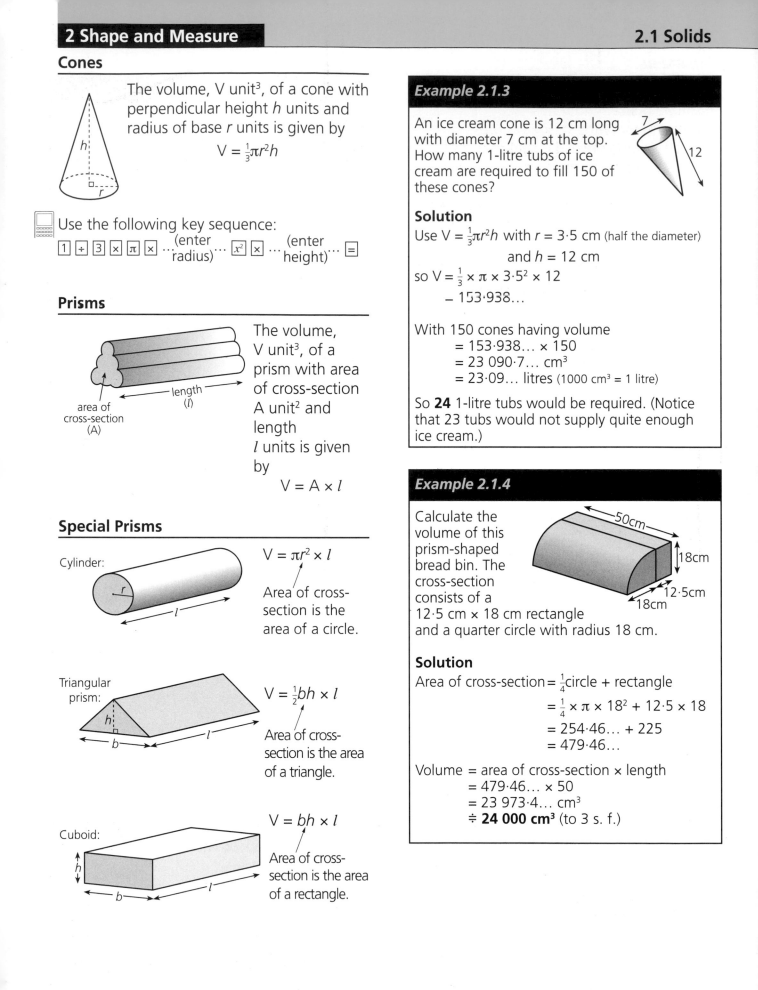

The volume, V unit³, of a cone with perpendicular height h units and radius of base r units is given by

$$V = \tfrac{1}{3}\pi r^2 h$$

Use the following key sequence:

[1] [÷] [3] [×] [π] [×] ⋯(enter radius)⋯ [x^2] [×] ⋯(enter height)⋯ [=]

Prisms

The volume, V unit³, of a prism with area of cross-section A unit² and length l units is given by

$$V = A \times l$$

area of cross-section (A)   length (l)

Special Prisms

Cylinder:

$$V = \pi r^2 \times l$$

Area of cross-section is the area of a circle.

Triangular prism:

$$V = \tfrac{1}{2}bh \times l$$

Area of cross-section is the area of a triangle.

Cuboid:

$$V = bh \times l$$

Area of cross-section is the area of a rectangle.

Example 2.1.3

An ice cream cone is 12 cm long with diameter 7 cm at the top. How many 1-litre tubs of ice cream are required to fill 150 of these cones?

Solution

Use $V = \tfrac{1}{3}\pi r^2 h$ with r = 3·5 cm (half the diameter) and h = 12 cm

so $V = \tfrac{1}{3} \times \pi \times 3\cdot5^2 \times 12$

    – 153·938…

With 150 cones having volume
= 153·938… × 150
= 23 090·7… cm³
= 23·09… litres (1000 cm³ = 1 litre)

So **24** 1-litre tubs would be required. (Notice that 23 tubs would not supply quite enough ice cream.)

Example 2.1.4

Calculate the volume of this prism-shaped bread bin. The cross-section consists of a 12·5 cm × 18 cm rectangle and a quarter circle with radius 18 cm.

Solution

Area of cross-section $= \tfrac{1}{4}$circle + rectangle

$= \tfrac{1}{4} \times \pi \times 18^2 + 12\cdot5 \times 18$

$= 254\cdot46… + 225$

$= 479\cdot46…$

Volume = area of cross-section × length
= 479·46… × 50
= 23 973·4… cm³
≑ **24 000 cm³** (to 3 s. f.)

Similarity

Shapes and solids may be enlarged or reduced in size. When this is done with all measurements kept in proportion, the resulting shape or solid is said to be mathematically **similar** to the original.

Similar shapes have corresponding angles equal and sides in the same proportion.

The number given by $\frac{\text{new length}}{\text{old length}}$ is called the scale factor and is usually denoted by k.

For reductions: $0 < k < 1$
(the scale factor, k, lies between 0 and 1)
For enlargements: $k > 1$
(the scale factor, k, is greater than 1)

For example, here is a triangle enlarged (k > 1):

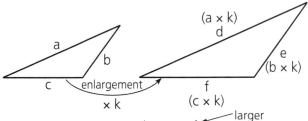

The scale factor $k = \frac{d}{a} = \frac{e}{b} = \frac{f}{c}$ ⟵ larger ⟵ smaller

Here is the triangle reduced (0 < k < 1)

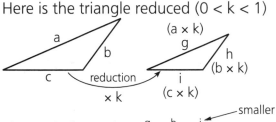

The scale factor $k = \frac{g}{a} = \frac{h}{b} = \frac{i}{c}$ ⟵ smaller ⟵ larger

Area and Volume and Similarity

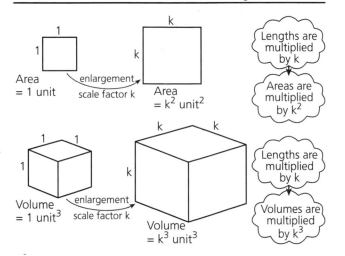

Lengths are multiplied by k

Areas are multiplied by k^2

Lengths are multiplied by k

Volumes are multiplied by k^3

Example 2.2.1

Emma, who is 1·9 m tall, stands $10\frac{1}{2}$m from the base of a tree. She notices that her 3 metre long shadow reaches exactly as far as the tree's shadow reaches. How tall is the tree?

Solution
Here is the diagram:

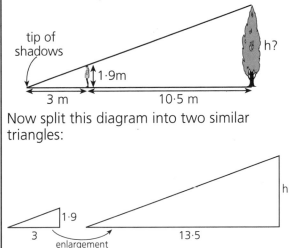

Now split this diagram into two similar triangles:

Scale factor $= \frac{13\cdot5}{3} = 4\cdot5$

This means that any length in the large triangle is 4·5 times the corresponding length in the small triangle.

So h = 1·9 × 4·5 = 8·55

The tree is **8m 55cm** high.

Example 2.2.2

These two bottles are mathematically similar. The volume of the smaller bottle is 80 cl. Find the volume of the larger in litres.

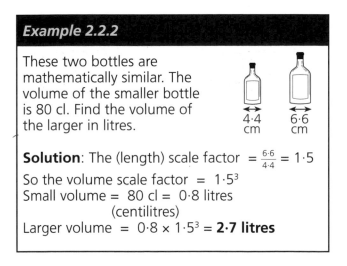

Solution: The (length) scale factor $= \frac{6\cdot6}{4\cdot4} = 1\cdot5$

So the volume scale factor $= 1\cdot5^3$
Small volume = 80 cl = 0·8 litres
(centilitres)
Larger volume = $0\cdot8 \times 1\cdot5^3$ = **2·7 litres**

Pythagoras' Theorem (reminder)

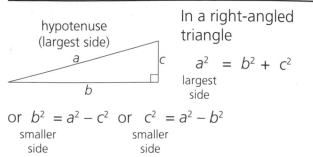

In a right-angled triangle

$$a^2 = b^2 + c^2$$

largest side

or $b^2 = a^2 - c^2$ or $c^2 = a^2 - b^2$

smaller side   smaller side

Note (1)

To find the hypotenuse (largest side), **add** the squares of the smaller sides, then find the square root. (Use ☑ button on calculator.)

Note (2)

To find a smaller side, **subtract** the squares of the other two sides (largest minus smallest), then find the square root. (Use ☑ button.)

The Converse of Pythagoras' Theorem

The Theorem:

Given   **Result**

$$a^2 = b^2 + c^2$$

A right-angled triangle

The Converse:

Result   **Given**

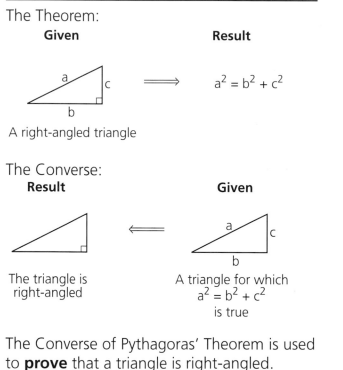

The triangle is right-angled

A triangle for which $a^2 = b^2 + c^2$ is true

The Converse of Pythagoras' Theorem is used to **prove** that a triangle is right-angled.

Example 2.3.1

Calculate BC to 1 d. p.

Solution

$$BD^2 = 10^2 - 8^2$$
$$= 100 - 64 = 36$$

So $BD = \sqrt{36} = 6$

$$BC^2 = 6^2 + 3^2$$
$$= 36 + 9$$
$$= 45$$

So $BC = \sqrt{45} = 6 \cdot 708\ldots$

giving BC ≑ **6·7 cm** (to 1 d. p.)

Example 2.3.2

A picture frame has dimensions 18·6 cm × 24·8 cm. There is doubt about whether it is rectangular or not, so the diagonal was measured and found to be 31 cm. Is it rectangular?

Solution

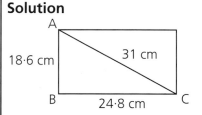

$$AB^2 + BC^2 = 18 \cdot 6^2 + 24 \cdot 8^2 = 961$$

Now compare this result with:

$$AC^2 = 31^2 = 961$$

So $AB^2 + BC^2 = AC^2$ and by the Converse of Pythagoras' Theorem, triangle ABC is right-angled at B.

The frame is indeed rectangular.

Circle Formulae (reminder)

Diameter = 2 × radius (D = 2*r*)

Circumference = π × diameter (C = πD)
where π = 3·14159...

In calculations, always use the $\boxed{\pi}$ button on your calculator.

Area of circle = π × radius × radius (A = π*r*²)

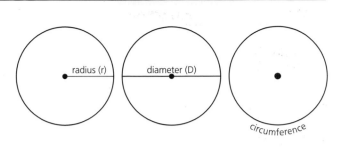

Finding Arcs and Sectors

A circle with centre O:

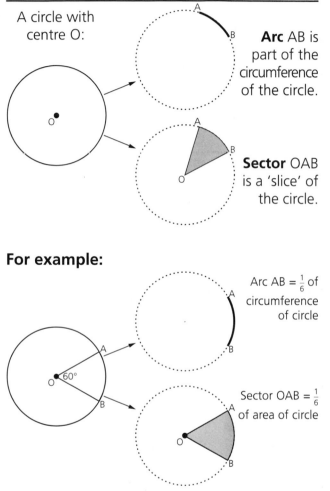

Arc AB is part of the circumference of the circle.

Sector OAB is a 'slice' of the circle.

For example:

Arc AB = $\frac{1}{6}$ of circumference of circle

Sector OAB = $\frac{1}{6}$ of area of circle

The 'circle fraction' $\frac{1}{6}$ is determined by the 60° angle at the centre. A complete turn is 360° and 60° is $\frac{60}{360} = \frac{1}{6}$ of this complete turn.

In general:

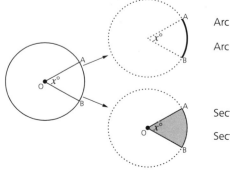

Arc AB = a fraction of circumference of circle

Arc AB = $\frac{x}{360}$ × πD

Sector OAB = a fraction of area of circle

Sector OAB = $\frac{x}{360}$ × π*r*²

Example 2.4.1

Find:
(a) The length of arc AB
(b) The area of sector OAB

Solution
(a) Arc AB = a fraction of circumference of circle

Arc AB = $\frac{110}{360}$ × π × 20 (diameter)

= 19·198...

≐ **19·2 cm** (to 1 d. p.)

(b) Sector OAB = a fraction of area of circle

Sector OAB = $\frac{110}{360}$ × π × 10² (radius)

= 95·993...

≐ **96·0 cm²** (to 1 d. p.)

Finding the angle at the centre

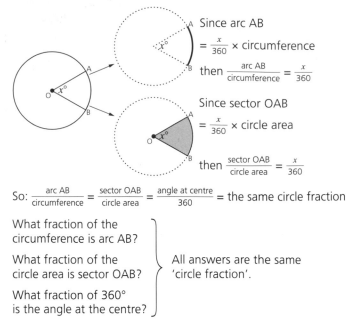

Since arc AB

$= \frac{x}{360} \times$ circumference

then $\frac{\text{arc AB}}{\text{circumference}} = \frac{x}{360}$

Since sector OAB

$= \frac{x}{360} \times$ circle area

then $\frac{\text{sector OAB}}{\text{circle area}} = \frac{x}{360}$

So: $\frac{\text{arc AB}}{\text{circumference}} = \frac{\text{sector OAB}}{\text{circle area}} = \frac{\text{angle at centre}}{360} =$ the same circle fraction

What fraction of the
circumference is arc AB?

What fraction of the
circle area is sector OAB?

What fraction of 360°
is the angle at the centre?

} All answers are the same
'circle fraction'.

Find this 'circle fraction' to solve 'angle at the
centre' problems.

Example 2.4.2

A sector of area 8 m² was removed
from a 10 m diameter clock face
for repair. Find, to 1 d. p., the
angle at the centre of the sector.

Solution
The 'circle fraction' in this case is:
$\frac{\text{sector OAB}}{\text{circle area}} = \frac{8}{\pi \times 5^2} = 0.1018...$

(radius)

So angle at centre $=$ circle fraction $\times$ 360
$= 0.1018... \times 360$
$= 36.66...$
$\doteq \mathbf{36.7°}$ (to 1 d. p.)

Tangent Properties

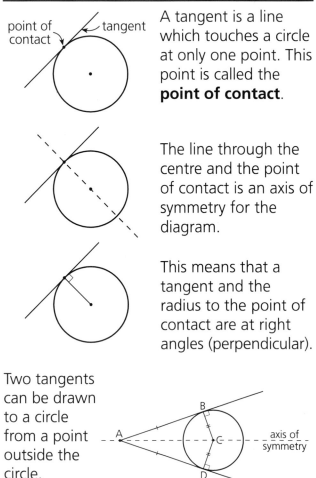

A tangent is a line
which touches a circle
at only one point. This
point is called the
point of contact.

The line through the
centre and the point
of contact is an axis of
symmetry for the
diagram.

This means that a
tangent and the
radius to the point of
contact are at right
angles (perpendicular).

Two tangents
can be drawn
to a circle
from a point
outside the
circle.

In the diagram, tangents AB and AD and the
two radii CB and CD form a kite ABCD.

Example 2.4.3

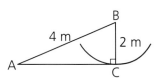

A cylindrical drum of
radius 2 m is held in place
by triangular metal
supports on each side as
shown. Rod AB is 4 m
long and attached to the
centre of the circle B,
directly above C. How many triangular metal
frames like ABC can be made from a 100 m
length of rod?

Solution

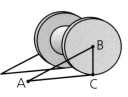

BC = 2 m (radius)
∠BCA = 90° (angle
between tangent AC and
radius BC)

So AC² = 4² − 2² = 16 − 4 = 12
giving AC = $\sqrt{12}$ = 3.46...

Length of rod in one frame = 4 + 2 + 3.46...
= 9.46...

Total no. of frames = $\frac{100}{9.46}$ = 10.56...

10 frames only
(Don't round up since 11 frames would require over
100 m of rod.)

Angles in a Semicircle

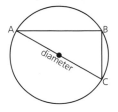

∠ABC is called an angle in a semicircle.

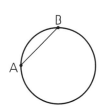

All angles in a semicircle are right-angles (90°).

Symmetry and Chords

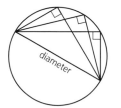

A line joining two points on a circumference is called a **chord**. The diameter is a special chord that passes through the centre. It is the longest possible chord.

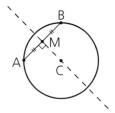

The axis of symmetry of the diagram passes through M, the midpoint of chord AB, and through the centre C. It is perpendicular to chord AB and bisects it (AM = MB).

Example 2.4.4

In an old semicircular tunnel of diameter 10 m, a roof support AB is 8 m long. Find the length of support CB.

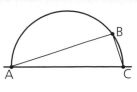

Solution

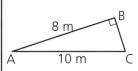

∠ABC = 90°
(It is an angle in a semicircle.)

Using Pythagoras' Theorem gives:

BC² = 10² − 8² = 100 − 64 = 36

So BC = √36 = **6 m**

Example 2.4.5

A circular table of diameter 1·4 m is hinged to the wall along AB as shown. The table, when up, extends 1·3 m out from the wall. What length of hinge is required?

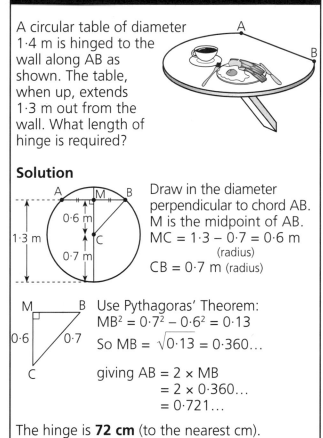

Solution

Draw in the diameter perpendicular to chord AB. M is the midpoint of AB.
MC = 1·3 − 0·7 = 0·6 m (radius)
CB = 0·7 m (radius)

Use Pythagoras' Theorem:
MB² = 0·7² − 0·6² = 0·13
So MB = √0·13 = 0·360…

giving AB = 2 × MB
= 2 × 0·360…
= 0·721…

The hinge is **72 cm** (to the nearest cm).

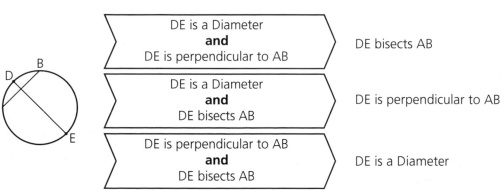

	Given	Result
	DE is a Diameter **and** DE is perpendicular to AB	DE bisects AB
	DE is a Diameter **and** DE bisects AB	DE is perpendicular to AB
	DE is perpendicular to AB **and** DE bisects AB	DE is a Diameter

Right-angled Triangles (reminder)

The sides of a right-angled triangle are named from the viewpoint of one of the angles.

The hypotenuse (the largest side) is always opposite the right-angle.

Reminder

Use sin if Opp and Hyp are known or required.

Use cos if Adj and Hyp are known or required.

Use tan if Opp and Adj are known or required.

Note

At all times your calculator display should show **D** or **DEG** not **R** or **RAD** or **G** or **GRAD**. Otherwise change **MODE** to **DEGREE**.

Here are three common types of problem.

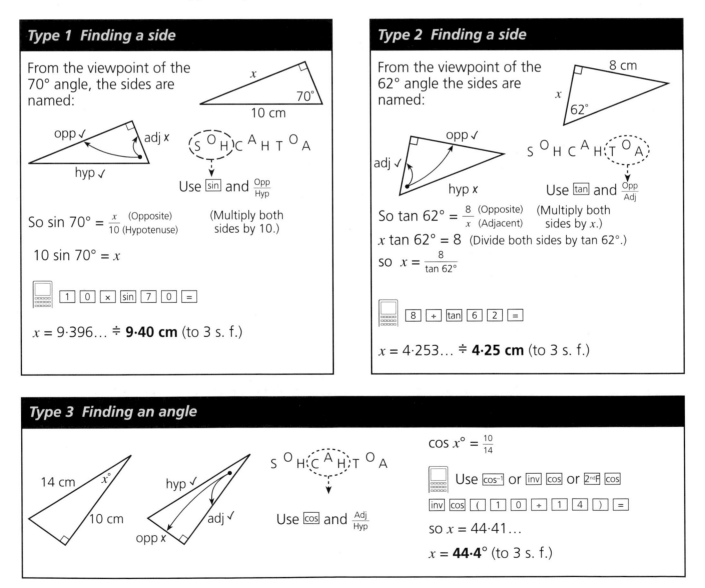

Type 1 Finding a side

From the viewpoint of the 70° angle, the sides are named:

Use sin and $\frac{\text{Opp}}{\text{Hyp}}$

So $\sin 70° = \frac{x}{10}$ (Opposite)/(Hypotenuse)   (Multiply both sides by 10.)

$10 \sin 70° = x$

$1\ 0 \times \sin 7\ 0 =$

$x = 9{\cdot}396\ldots \doteqdot \mathbf{9{\cdot}40\ cm}$ (to 3 s. f.)

Type 2 Finding a side

From the viewpoint of the 62° angle the sides are named:

Use tan and $\frac{\text{Opp}}{\text{Adj}}$

So $\tan 62° = \frac{8}{x}$ (Opposite)/(Adjacent)   (Multiply both sides by x.)

$x \tan 62° = 8$ (Divide both sides by $\tan 62°$.)

so $x = \frac{8}{\tan 62°}$

$8 \div \tan 6\ 2 =$

$x = 4{\cdot}253\ldots \doteqdot \mathbf{4{\cdot}25\ cm}$ (to 3 s. f.)

Type 3 Finding an angle

Use cos and $\frac{\text{Adj}}{\text{Hyp}}$

$\cos x° = \frac{10}{14}$

Use cos⁻¹ or inv cos or 2ndF cos

inv cos (1 0 ÷ 1 4) =

so $x = 44{\cdot}41\ldots$

$x = \mathbf{44{\cdot}4}°$ (to 3 s. f.)

Angles greater than 90°

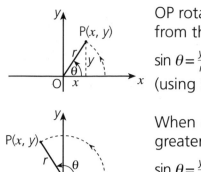

OP rotates about O from the x-axis by $\theta°$.

$\sin \theta = \frac{y}{r}$ $\cos \theta = \frac{x}{r}$ $\tan \theta = \frac{y}{x}$

(using $S^OHC^AHT^OA$).

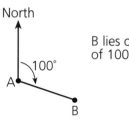

When $\theta°$ becomes greater than 90° then:

$\sin \theta = \frac{y}{r}$ $\cos \theta = \frac{x}{r}$ $\tan \theta = \frac{y}{x}$

can still be used to calculate the values of $\sin \theta$, $\cos \theta$ and $\tan \theta$.

Example 3.1.1

Use your calculator to find the following to 3 s. f.
(a) sin 23°
(b) cos 123°
(c) tan 224°

Solution
(a) $\sin 23° = 0{\cdot}3907\ldots \doteqdot \mathbf{0{\cdot}391}$ (to 3 s. f.)
(b) $\cos 123° = -0{\cdot}5446\ldots \doteqdot \mathbf{-0{\cdot}545}$ (to 3 s. f.)
(c) $\tan 224° = 0{\cdot}9656\ldots \doteqdot \mathbf{0{\cdot}966}$ (to 3 s. f.)

3.2 Three-figure Bearings

Three-figure Bearings

North

B lies on a bearing of 100° from A.

From location A, the direction you need to travel to get to location B may be described by an angle. Here are the steps:

step 1   Stand at A and face north
step 2   Turn clockwise to face B
step 3   Measure the angle through which you turned

This angle is the **bearing** of B from A.

Note
Three digits are always used to describe a bearing. So, for example, 028° is used for the angle 28°.

Example 3.2.1

The bearing of a lighthouse from a ship is 053°. Calculate the bearing of the ship from the lighthouse.

Solution

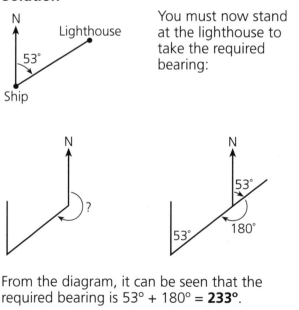

You must now stand at the lighthouse to take the required bearing:

From the diagram, it can be seen that the required bearing is 53° + 180° = **233°**.

Naming the sides of a triangle

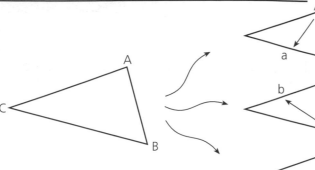

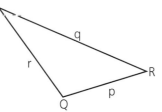

The small letters used for the sides match the capital letters used for the opposite angles as shown in this diagram.

Here are other examples:

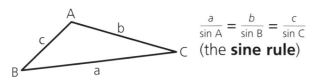

Area of a Triangle

If the triangle is right-angled:

Area = $\frac{1}{2}bh$

If you know the height: Area = $\frac{1}{2}bh$

If you know two sides and the angle included between these sides:

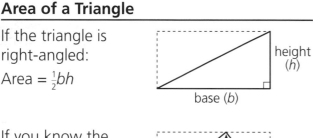

Area = $\frac{1}{2}ab \sin C$ or $\frac{1}{2}ac \sin B$ or $\frac{1}{2}bc \sin A$.

The Sine Rule

In **any** triangle ABC:

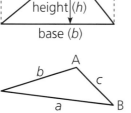

$$\frac{a}{\sin A} = \frac{b}{\sin B} = \frac{c}{\sin C}$$

(the **sine rule**)

How do you know when to use the sine rule?

Your problem will involve two pairs of 'opposites':

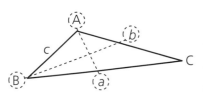

If any three of ∠A, ∠B, a and b are known then the fourth can be calculated using the sine rule.

Example 3.3.1

80 cm

32°

90 cm

Calculate the area of this triangular flag.

Solution

Area = $\frac{1}{2} \times 80 \times 90 \times \sin 32°$

= 1907·70…

≐ **1910 cm²** (to 3 s. f.)

Example 3.3.2

Calculate PR in triangle PQR.

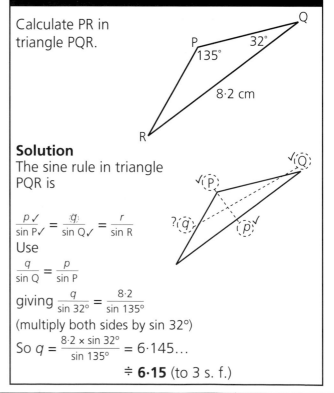

Solution

The sine rule in triangle PQR is

$$\frac{p\,✓}{\sin P\,✓} = \frac{q}{\sin Q\,✓} = \frac{r}{\sin R}$$

Use

$$\frac{q}{\sin Q} = \frac{p}{\sin P}$$

giving $\dfrac{q}{\sin 32°} = \dfrac{8·2}{\sin 135°}$

(multiply both sides by sin 32°)

So $q = \dfrac{8·2 \times \sin 32°}{\sin 135°} = 6·145…$

≐ **6·15** (to 3 s. f.)

Example 3.3.3

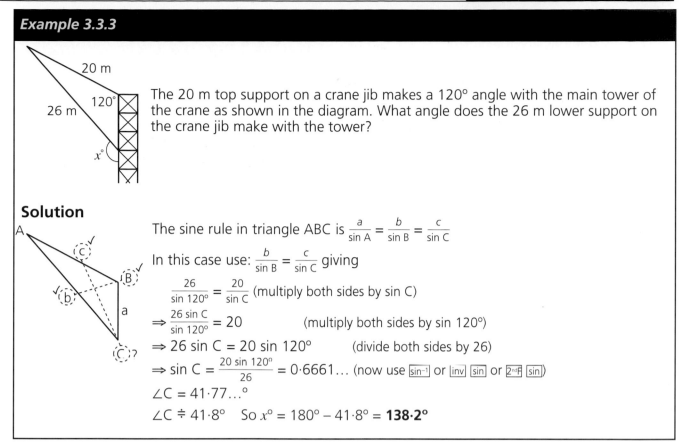

The 20 m top support on a crane jib makes a 120° angle with the main tower of the crane as shown in the diagram. What angle does the 26 m lower support on the crane jib make with the tower?

Solution

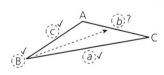

The sine rule in triangle ABC is $\frac{a}{\sin A} = \frac{b}{\sin B} = \frac{c}{\sin C}$

In this case use: $\frac{b}{\sin B} = \frac{c}{\sin C}$ giving

$\frac{26}{\sin 120°} = \frac{20}{\sin C}$ (multiply both sides by sin C)

$\Rightarrow \frac{26 \sin C}{\sin 120°} = 20$ (multiply both sides by sin 120°)

$\Rightarrow 26 \sin C = 20 \sin 120°$ (divide both sides by 26)

$\Rightarrow \sin C = \frac{20 \sin 120°}{26} = 0·6661...$ (now use $\boxed{\sin^{-1}}$ or $\boxed{\text{inv}}$ $\boxed{\sin}$ or $\boxed{2^{nd}F}$ $\boxed{\sin}$)

$\angle C = 41·77...°$

$\angle C \doteqdot 41·8°$ So $x° = 180° − 41·8° = \textbf{138·2°}$

The Cosine Rule (finding a side)

In **any** triangle ABC

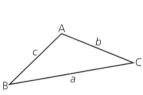

$$a^2 = b^2 + c^2 − 2bc \cos A$$
or
$$b^2 = a^2 + c^2 − 2ac \cos B$$
or
$$c^2 = b^2 + a^2 − 2ba \cos C$$
(the **cosine rule**)

How do you know when to use the cosine rule? Your problem will involve knowing two sides and the angle included between these sides:

If you know the two sides and the included angle you can find the side opposite this angle. (In the case shown on the left, use $b^2 = a^2 + c^2 − 2ac \cos B$)

Example 3.3.4

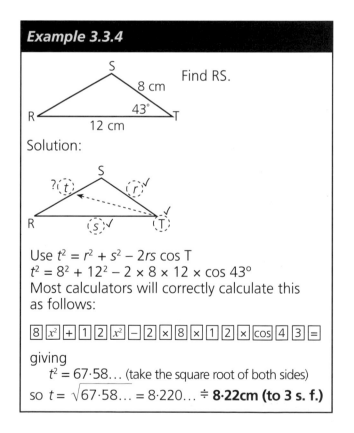

Find RS.

Solution:

Use $t^2 = r^2 + s^2 − 2rs \cos T$
$t^2 = 8^2 + 12^2 − 2 × 8 × 12 × \cos 43°$
Most calculators will correctly calculate this as follows:

$\boxed{8}\boxed{x^2}\boxed{+}\boxed{1}\boxed{2}\boxed{x^2}\boxed{-}\boxed{2}\boxed{×}\boxed{8}\boxed{×}\boxed{1}\boxed{2}\boxed{×}\boxed{\cos}\boxed{4}\boxed{3}\boxed{=}$

giving
    $t^2 = 67·58...$ (take the square root of both sides)
so $t = \sqrt{67·58...} = 8·220... \doteqdot \textbf{8·22cm (to 3 s. f.)}$

The Cosine Rule (finding an angle)

The cosine rule has another form:
In **any** triangle ABC

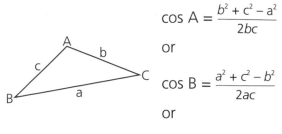

$$\cos A = \frac{b^2 + c^2 - a^2}{2bc}$$

or

$$\cos B = \frac{a^2 + c^2 - b^2}{2ac}$$

or

$$\cos C = \frac{a^2 + b^2 - c^2}{2ab}$$

This form of the cosine rule allows you to find an angle if you know all three sides.

Example 3.3.5

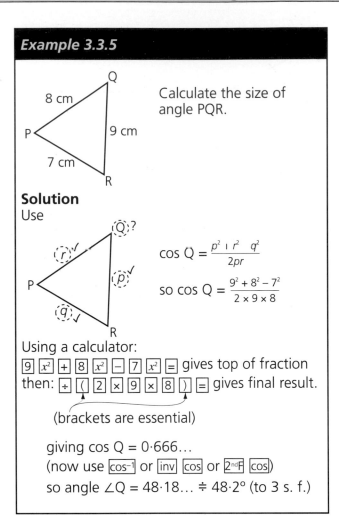

Calculate the size of angle PQR.

Solution
Use

$$\cos Q = \frac{p^2 + r^2 - q^2}{2pr}$$

so $\cos Q = \dfrac{9^2 + 8^2 - 7^2}{2 \times 9 \times 8}$

Using a calculator:

9 x^2 + 8 x^2 − 7 x^2 = gives top of fraction
then: ÷ (2 × 9 × 8) = gives final result.

(brackets are essential)

giving $\cos Q = 0{\cdot}666\ldots$
(now use cos⁻¹ or inv cos or 2ndF cos)
so angle $\angle Q = 48{\cdot}18\ldots \doteq 48{\cdot}2°$ (to 3 s. f.)

The Sine, Cosine and Tangent Graphs

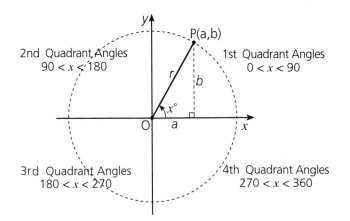

From a starting position along the x-axis, line OP rotates about the origin O anticlockwise $x°$ as shown in the diagram.
Here are three definitions:

$$\sin x° = \frac{b}{r} \qquad \cos x° = \frac{a}{r} \qquad \tan x° = \frac{b}{a}$$

Since a and b are coordinates they may be positive or negative.
r is the length of OP so is always positive.

You can draw graphs showing the values of these three **trigonometric functions** $\sin x°$, $\cos x°$ and $\tan x°$ as OP rotates from 0° through all 4 quadrants to 360°:

$y = \sin x°$

+ ve | + ve
− ve | − ve

$\sin x°$ is positive in the 1st and 2nd quadrants.

$\sin 0° = 0$ $\sin 90° = 1$ $\sin 180° = 0$ $\sin 270° = -1$ $\sin 360° = 0$

$y = \cos x°$

− ve | + ve
− ve | + ve

$\cos x°$ is positive in the 1st and 4th quadrants.

$\cos 0° = 1$ $\cos 90° = 0$ $\cos 180° - -1$ $\cos 270° = 0$ $\cos 360° = 1$

$y = \tan x°$

− ve | + ve
+ ve | − ve

$\tan x°$ is positive in the 1st and 3rd quadrants.

$\tan 0° = 0$ $\tan 90°$ $\tan 180° = 0$ $\tan 270°$ $\tan 360° = 0$
          is undefined   is undefined

The summary diagram:

S	A
T	C

indicates that for angles $x°$ in the
1st quadrant: $\sin x°$, $\cos x°$, $\tan x°$ are **A**ll positive (**A**) ($0 < x < 90$)

2nd quadrant: only **S**in $x°$ is positive (**S**) ($90 < x < 180$)

3rd quadrant: only **T**an $x°$ is positive (**T**) ($180 < x < 270$)

4th quadrant: only **C**os $x°$ is positive (**C**) ($270 < x < 360$)

Example 3.4.1

On the same diagram sketch the graphs $y = \cos x°$ and $y = \sin x°$ for $0 \leqslant x \leqslant 360$.

Solution

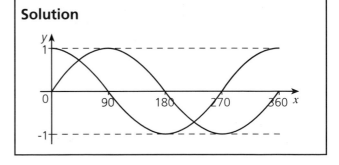

Related Graphs

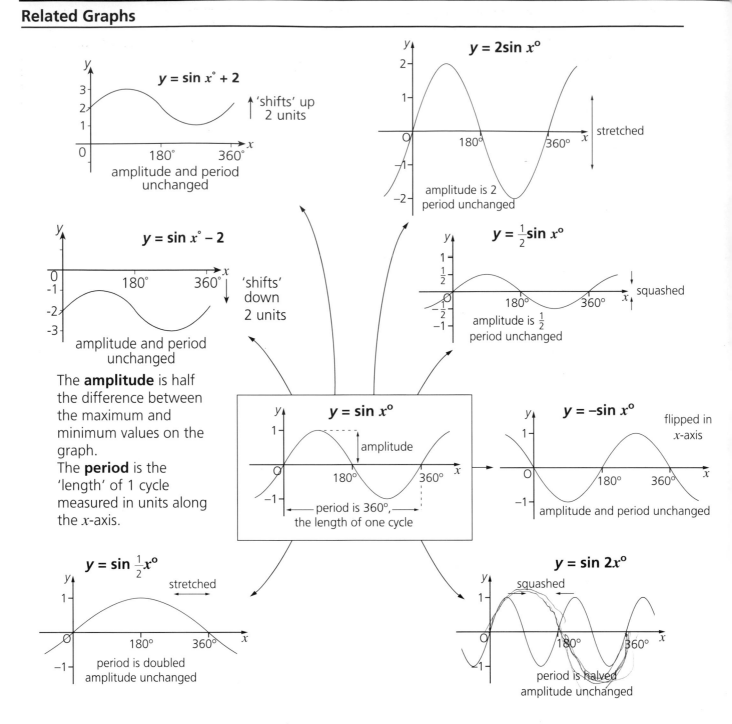

$y = \sin x° + 2$

'shifts' up 2 units

amplitude and period unchanged

$y = 2\sin x°$

stretched

amplitude is 2 period unchanged

$y = \sin x° - 2$

'shifts' down 2 units

amplitude and period unchanged

$y = \frac{1}{2}\sin x°$

squashed

amplitude is $\frac{1}{2}$ period unchanged

The **amplitude** is half the difference between the maximum and minimum values on the graph.

The **period** is the 'length' of 1 cycle measured in units along the x-axis.

$y = \sin x°$

amplitude

period is 360°, the length of one cycle

$y = -\sin x°$

flipped in x-axis

amplitude and period unchanged

$y = \sin \frac{1}{2}x°$

stretched

period is doubled amplitude unchanged

$y = \sin 2x°$

squashed

period is halved amplitude unchanged

Here is a summary showing how the graphs of $y = \sin x°$ and $y = \cos x°$ are altered by various changes to the graph formulae:

$$y = k \sin ax° \pm b$$
$$y = k \cos ax° \pm b$$

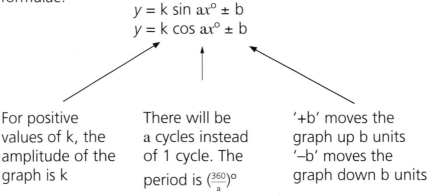

For positive values of k, the amplitude of the graph is k

There will be a cycles instead of 1 cycle. The period is $\left(\frac{360}{a}\right)°$

'+b' moves the graph up b units
'−b' moves the graph down b units

Example 3.4.2

The diagram shows the graph
$$y = k \sin ax°$$

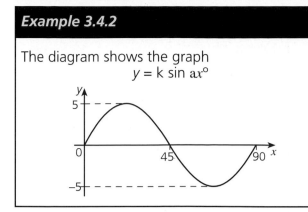

(a) State the values of k and a.
(b) Give the maximum and minimum values of k sin ax°.
(c) State the period of the graph.

Solution
(a) The amplitude is 5 so k = 5. From the x-axis scale there will be 4 cycles from 0° to 360° so a = 4.
(b) The maximum is 5 and the minimum is −5.
(c) The period is 90°.

3.5 Trig Equations and Formulae

Solving Simple Trig Equations

step 1 Rearrange to get $\frac{\sin, \cos}{\text{or} \tan}$ (angle) = number

step 2 Decide which quadrants the angle is in by using the quadrant diagram:

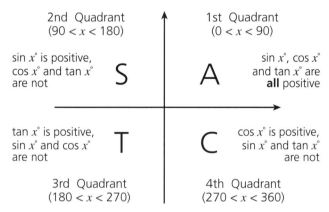

2nd Quadrant (90 < x < 180) 1st Quadrant (0 < x < 90)

sin x° is positive, cos x° and tan x° are not **S**   **A** sin x°, cos x° and tan x° are **all** positive

tan x° is positive, sin x° and cos x° are not **T**   **C** cos x° is positive, sin x° and tan x° are not

3rd Quadrant (180 < x < 270) 4th Quadrant (270 < x < 360)

step 3 Find the 1st quadrant angle using the positive value of the number (use [sin⁻¹], [cos⁻¹] or [tan⁻¹] on your calculator as necessary).

step 4 Calculate the required values of the angle using:

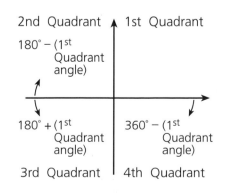

2nd Quadrant   1st Quadrant

180° − (1st Quadrant angle)

180° + (1st Quadrant angle)   360° − (1st Quadrant angle)

3rd Quadrant   4th Quadrant

Note
Special equations like:
$$\sin x° = 1, \quad \sin x° = 0, \quad \sin x° = -1$$
$$\text{or } \cos x° = 1, \quad \cos x° = 0, \quad \cos x° = -1$$
are solved by looking at the graph $y = \sin x°$ or $y = \cos x°$.

Example 3.5.1

Solve 2sin x° + 1 = 0, 0 < x < 360.

Solution
step 1 2sin x° + 1 = 0 rearranges to get
$$\sin x° = -\frac{1}{2}$$
step 2 sin x° is negative for angles in the 3rd and 4th quadrants.
step 3 The 1st quadrant angle is 30°.

step 4 x = 180 + 30 or   x = 360 − 30
(3rd quadrant)   (4th quadrant)
x = 210   **x = 330**

Note
A graphical check may be made using the $y = \sin x°$ graph:

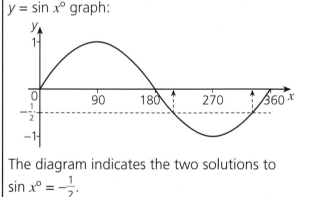

The diagram indicates the two solutions to $\sin x° = -\frac{1}{2}$.

Example 3.5.2

Solve $\cos x° = 0$ for $0 \leqslant x \leqslant 360$.

Solution

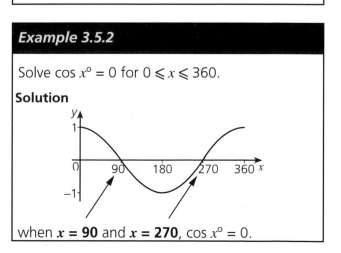

when **x = 90** and **x = 270**, cos x° = 0.

Some Trig Formulae

Here are two results that are true for all angles $x°$:

1. $\dfrac{\sin x°}{\cos x°} = \tan x°$

2. $\sin^2 x° + \cos^2 x° = 1$ ⟶ $\sin^2 x° = 1 - \cos^2 x°$

                              rearranging

                              ⟶ $\cos^2 x° = 1 - \sin^2 x°$

Note

$\sin^2 x°$ means $\sin x° \times \sin x°$

$\cos^2 x°$ means $\cos x° \times \cos x°$

Applications of Trig Formulae

Some situations, such as the water depth of a harbour, the height of a bouncing object on a spring, etc, have a naturally occurring cycle. These can often be described mathematically by using a trig formula:

$a + b \sin (cx)°$ or $a + b \cos (cx)°$

The example opposite illustrates how this is done.

Example 3.5.3

Show that $\dfrac{\sin^2 A}{1 - \sin^2 A} = \tan^2 A$

Solution

$\dfrac{\sin^2 A}{1 - \sin^2 A}$ Since $\sin^2 A + \cos^2 A = 1$ then $\cos^2 A = 1 - \sin^2 A$.

$= \dfrac{\sin^2 A}{\cos^2 A}$

$= \dfrac{\sin A}{\cos A} \times \dfrac{\sin A}{\cos A} = \tan A \times \tan A$

                           $= \mathbf{\tan^2 A}$ as required.

Example 3.5.4

The depth of water, D metres, at a harbour, t hours after midnight, is given by the formula:

$D = 13 + 8·5 \cos (30t)°$

(a) Find the depth at 3 p.m.
(b) Find the difference between the maximum and minimum depths over time.

Solution

(a) 3 p.m. is 15 hours after midnight, so t = 15 giving:
$D = 13 + 8·5 \cos (30 \times 15)°$
$= 13 + 8·5 \cos 450° = \mathbf{13}$ metres.

(b) The value of $\cos (30t)°$ ranges from 1 to −1 as the angle of $30t°$ changes value.

So the maximum depth is
$13 + 8·5 \times 1 = 21·5$ metres

And the minimum depth is
$13 + 8·5 \times (-1) = 4·5$ metres

The difference is $21·5 - 4·5 = \mathbf{17}$ metres.

Adding and Subtracting Terms

Use the number line:

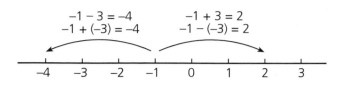

In the same way:

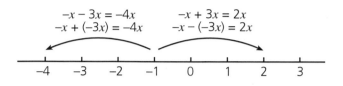

Example 4.1.1

Simplify: (a) $y - (-3y)$
              (b) $2x^2 + x - 5x^2$
              (c) $-3a \times 4a$
              (d) $-2x - 3x$

Solution

(a) $y - (-3y) = y + 3y = 4y$
    (Subtracting a negative is the same as adding.)

(b) $2x^2 + x - 5x^2 = -3x^2 + x$
    ($2x^2$ and x cannot be added together but
    '2 lots of x^2' minus '5 lots of x^2' gives
    'minus 3 lots of x^2')

(c) $-3a \times 4a = -12a^2$
    (neg)   (pos)   (neg)

(d) $-2x - 3x = -5x$

    compare: $-2 - 3 = -5$

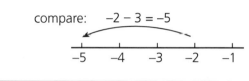

Multiplying Terms

Use the rules:

$\left.\begin{array}{l}\text{positive} \times \text{positive}\\\text{negative} \times \text{negative}\end{array}\right\}$ positive

$\left.\begin{array}{l}\text{negative} \times \text{positive}\\\text{positive} \times \text{negative}\end{array}\right\}$ negative

So $x \times (-3x) = -3x^2$ and $-2a \times (-3b) = 6ab$
    (pos) (neg) (neg)   (neg) (neg) (pos)

Ways of thinking and writing

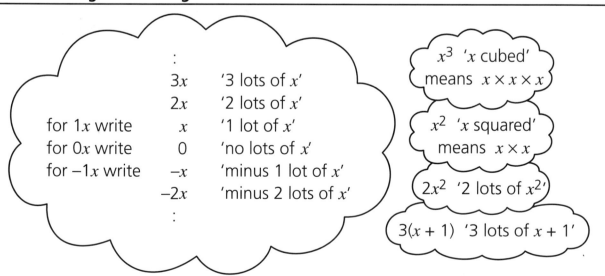

Function Notation

Here is an example of function notation and its meaning:

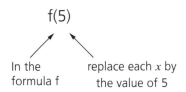

$$f(x) = x^2$$

Here is a function or formula called f.   It involves the variable x.   The formula is x^2.

You may now evaluate this function for a particular value of x:

f(5)

In the formula f   replace each x by the value of 5

This gives $f(5) = 5^2 = 25$

(Note: There is an alternative notation:
$$f : x \longrightarrow x^2$$
and $f : 5 \longrightarrow 5^2$)

Different letters may be used instead of f:

e.g. $g(x) = \sqrt{x}$, or $h(x) = \frac{6}{x}$, etc.

Example 4.1.2

Given that $f(n) = n^3 - 4n$, evaluate $f(-2)$

Solution
$f(n) = n^3 - 4n$
so $f(-2) = (-2)^3 - 4 \times (-2)$
$= -8 + 8 = 0$

Example 4.1.3

Two functions are defined by:

$f(x) = x^2$ and $g(x) = 2x$

Find the values of x for which $f(x) = g(x)$

Solution
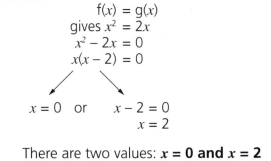
$$f(x) = g(x)$$
gives $x^2 = 2x$
$$x^2 - 2x = 0$$
$$x(x - 2) = 0$$

$x = 0$ or $x - 2 = 0$
$x = 2$

There are two values: **$x = 0$ and $x = 2$**

Removing One Pair of Brackets

$3(x - 2)$ ▶means▶   '3 lots of $x - 2$'

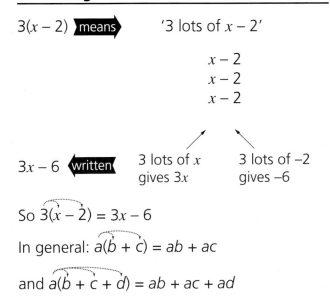

$x - 2$
$x - 2$
$x - 2$

$3x - 6$ ◀written◀   3 lots of x gives $3x$ 3 lots of -2 gives -6

So $3(x - 2) = 3x - 6$

In general: $a(b + c) = ab + ac$

and $a(b + c + d) = ab + ac + ad$

Example 4.2.1

Write without brackets:
(a) $3(x + 2)$
(b) $-2(4 - y)$
(c) $-(x - x^2)$

Solution

(a) $3(x + 2) = \mathbf{3x + 6}$

(b) $-2(4 - y) = \mathbf{-8 + 2y}$

(c) $-(x - x^2)$ Think of $-1(x - x^2)$.
       $= \mathbf{-x + x^2}$

Removing Two Pairs of Brackets

	2	3
1	1×2	1×3
4	4×2	4×3

This square has area:

$$5 \times 5$$
$$= (1 + 4)(2 + 3)$$

or adding individual rectangles:

$$1 \times 2 + 1 \times 3 + 4 \times 2 + 4 \times 3$$

First numbers in each bracket | Outside two numbers | Inside two numbers | Last numbers in each bracket

The rule is **F O I L**

which means: **F**irsts, **O**utsides, **I**nsides, **L**asts

Here is the pattern in general:

$$(a + b)(c + d)$$

Firsts: $(a + b)(c + d)$ ac

Outsides: $(a + b)(c + d)$ ad

Insides: $(a + b)(c + d)$ bc

Lasts: $(a + b)(c + d)$ bd

giving: $ac + ad + bc + bd$

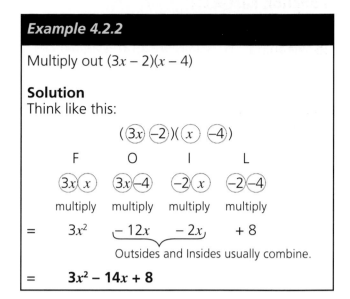

Example 4.2.2

Multiply out $(3x - 2)(x - 4)$

Solution
Think like this:

$$(3x \; -2)(x \; -4)$$

    F   O   I   L

$3x \cdot x$ $3x \cdot -4$ $-2 \cdot x$ $-2 \cdot -4$

multiply   multiply   multiply   multiply

$= \quad 3x^2 \quad -12x \quad -2x \quad +8$

Outsides and Insides usually combine.

$= \quad \mathbf{3x^2 - 14x + 8}$

Brackets Squared

Remember that a^2 means $a \times a$. So for examples like:

$$(2x - 1)^2 \qquad (a - b)^2$$
$$(2 + y)^2$$

you should write out a pair of equal brackets:

$(2x - 1)^2$ becomes $(2x - 1)(2x - 1)$
$(a - b)^2$ becomes $(a - b)(a - b)$

and $(2 + y)^2$ becomes $(2 + y)(2 + y)$

Example 4.2.3

Multiply out the brackets and collect like terms:
$(2x - 5)^2 - x(x + 2)$

Solution
$$(2x - 5)(2x - 5) - x(x + 2)$$

$= \quad 4x^2 - 10x - 10x + 25 \underbrace{}_{} - x^2 - 2x$

Using FOIL   one pair
                  of brackets

$= \qquad \mathbf{3x^2 - 22x + 25}$

(from   (from
$4x^2 - x^2$) $-10x - 10x - 2x$)

Larger Brackets

For expressions such as:
$$(a + b)(c + d + e)$$
FOIL does not work.

Here is the pattern to use:

$(a + b)(c + d + e)$ giving $ac + ad + ae$

then $(a + b)(c + d + e)$ giving $bc + bd + be$

There is a total of six multiplications:

$$(a + b)(c + d + e) = ac + ad + ae + bc + bd + be$$

Example 4.2.4

Write without brackets:
$$(2x - 3)(x^2 + 2x - 5)$$

Solution
First multiply by $2x$

$(2x - 3)(x^2 + 2x - 5)$ giving $2x^3 + 4x^2 - 10x$

Now multiply by -3

$(2x - 3)(x^2 + 2x - 5)$ giving $-3x^2 - 6x + 15$

So $(2x - 3)(x^2 + 2x - 5)$

$= 2x^3 + 4x^2 - 10x$ (from $2x$)

$\quad -3x^2 - 6x + 15$ (from -3)

$= \mathbf{2x^3 + x^2 - 16x + 15}$

Common Factors

30 = 1 × 30 or 2 × 15 or 3 × 10 or 6 × 5
so the factors of 30 are 1, 2, 3, 5, 6, 10, 15 and 30.

Similarly
6a = 1 × 6a or 2 × 3a or 3 × 2a or 6 × a
so the factors of 6a are 1, 2, 3, 6, a, 2a, 3a and 6a.

Consider   30ab   +   6a

            factor 6a   factor 6a
            (6a × 5b)   (6a × 1)

So $30ab + 6a = 6a(5b + 1)$

The common factor 6a has been taken outside the brackets.

Here is another example:
$$6x^2 - 4x = 2x(3x - 2)$$

factor 2x factor 2x   The common factor 2x
$(2x × 3x)$ $(2x × 2)$ has been taken outside
                         the brackets.

Difference of Two Squares

The square numbers:

1 1^2 25 5^2 144 12^2 121 11^2 16 4^2 100 10^2
36 6^2 4 2^2 64 8^2 81 9^2 49 7^2

Pick any two and find the difference (subtract them), e.g.

$100 - 49 = 51$ $64 - 36 = 28$
$10^2 - 7^2 = 3 × 17$ or $8^2 - 6^2 = 2 × 14$
$10^2 - 7^2 = (10 - 7)(10 + 7)$ $8^2 - 6^2 = (8 - 6)(8 + 6)$

In general the pattern is:
$$a^2 - b^2 = (a - b)(a + b)$$

Example 4.3.1

Factorise:
(a) $8x - 6$
(b) $7x^2 - 21x$
(c) $12xy^2 + 9x^2y$

Solution
(a) $8x$ – 6   = **2(4x – 3)**
    $(2 × 4x)$ $(2 × 3)$ common factor 2

(b) $7x^2$ – $21x$ = **7x(x – 3)**
    $(7x × x)$ $(7x × 3)$ common factor 7x

(c) $12xy^2 + 9x^2y$ = **3xy(4y + 3x)**
    $(3xy × 4y)$ $(3xy × 3x)$ common factor 3xy

Example 4.3.2

Factorise:
(a) $k^2 - m^2$
(b) $9x^2 - 1$
(c) $16y^2 - 25z^2$

Solution
(a) $k^2 - m^2 =$ **(k – m)(k + m)**

(b) $9x^2 - 1$ This is $(3x)^2 - 1^2$
    = **(3x – 1)(3x + 1)**

(c) $16y^2 - 25z^2$ This is $(4y)^2 - (5z)^2$
    = **(4y – 5z)(4y + 5z)**

Quadratic Expressions

Multiplying out $(x + 2)(x + 3)$
gives $\qquad x^2 \quad + \quad 3x \quad + \quad 2x \quad + \quad 6$
(remember: $\qquad$ F $\qquad$ O $\qquad$ I $\qquad$ L)
and simplifies to $x^2 + 5x + 6$

Factorising $x^2 + 5x + 6$ reverses this process
to get: $(x + 2)(x + 3)$

Here's another example:
Factorise $x^2 - x - 6$

step 1 Choose suitable Firsts and Lasts:
$$x^2 \ldots\ldots 6$$
Firsts: $(x \quad)(x \quad) \quad x \times x = x^2$
Lasts: $(\quad 2)(\quad 3) \quad 2 \times 3 = 6$

step 2 Write down the Outsides and Insides:

$(x \quad 2)(x \quad 3)$ Outsides: $3x$

$(x \quad 2)(x \quad 3)$ Insides: $2x$

step 3 Add or subtract to make the middle
term:
$$x^2 \enspace \overset{\frown}{- x} \enspace - 6$$

$$2x - 3x$$
$\quad$ Insides $\qquad$ Outsides
$\quad$ positive $\qquad$ negative

* If this step fails, redo **step 1** with different
Firsts or Lasts (or swap the order of the
Lasts if it makes a difference!) and repeat.

step 4 Put in the signs and check:
$$x^2 - x - 6$$
$$= (x + 2)(x - 3) \text{ Multiply out}$$
$$\underset{\substack{\text{SUM}\\ \text{NEGATIVE}}}{\underbrace{\qquad\qquad}} \text{ using FOIL to check.}$$

* If the check fails, redo **step 1** with different
Firsts or Lasts (or swap the order of the
Lasts if it makes a difference!) and repeat.

Example 4.3.3

Factorise: $x^2 - 10x + 16$

Solution

step 1	$(x \quad 4)(x \quad 4)$
step 2	Outsides: $4x$ Insides: $4x$
step 3	Middle term $-10x$ cannot be made from $4x$ and $4x$
step 1 again	$(x \quad 2)(x \quad 8)$
step 2	Outsides: $8x$ Insides: $2x$
step 3	Middle term $-10x$ is $-8x - 2x$
step 4	$(x - 2)(x - 8)$ and multiplying out gives: $x^2 - 10x + 16$

Example 4.3.4

Factorise: $6x^2 + x - 2$

Solution

step 1	$(2x \quad 2)(3x \quad 1)$
step 2	Outsides: $2x$ Insides: $6x$
step 3	Middle term x cannot be made from $2x$ and $6x$
step 1 again	$(2x \quad 1)(3x \quad 2)$
step 2	Outsides: $4x$ Insides: $3x$
step 3	Middle term x is $4x - 3x$
step 4	$(2x - 1)(3x + 2)$ Check this by multiplying out.

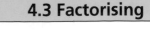
Factorising Fully

$$30 = 2 \times 15$$

However, 15 can be factorised further giving: $30 = 2 \times 3 \times 5$

Similarly:
$$8x^2 - 2y^2$$
$$= 2(4x^2 - y^2)$$

However, $4x^2 - y^2$ can be factorised further because it is a difference of squares, giving:

$$2(2x - y)(2x + y)$$

which is now factorised fully.

Example 4.3.5

Factorise fully:
(a) $2x^2 - 14x + 24$
(b) $3x^4 - 48$

Solution
(a) $2x^2 - 14x + 24$ common factor 2
$= 2(x^2 - 7x + 12)$ quadratic
$\mathbf{= 2(x - 3)(x - 4)}$

(b) $3x^4 - 48$ common factor 3
$= 3(x^4 - 16)$ difference of squares: $(x^2)^2$ 4^2
$= 3(x^2 - 4)(x^2 + 4)$ difference of squares: $x^2 - 2^2$
$\mathbf{= 3(x - 2)(x + 2)(x^2 + 4)}$

4.4 Solving Linear Equations

Solving Linear Equations

The golden rule when solving linear equations (i.e. equations with no terms in x^2 or x^3, etc.) is to balance the equation.

This means: Do the same operation to both sides of the equation.

The aim is to obtain the letter on its own, e.g. $x = \ldots$ or $\ldots = x$.

Here is an example:

$$3x + 2 = x - 6$$
$$(-x) \qquad (-x)$$

gives $2x + 2 = -6$
$$(-2) \quad (-2)$$

gives $2x = -8$
$$(\div 2) \quad (\div 2)$$

gives $x = -4$

In general the steps are as follows:

step 1   Remove fractions if there are any by multiplying both sides by a suitable number.

step 2   Remove any brackets and simplify each side if possible.

step 3   Proceed with balancing operations to get the letter on its own.

Example 4.4.1

Solve (a) $\frac{3}{4}x = 2$ (b) $5x - 3(x - 1) = 2$

Solution

(a) $\frac{3}{4}x = 2$
   $(\times 4) \quad (\times 4)$

$3x = 8$
$(\div 3) \quad (\div 3)$

$x = \frac{8}{3}$

$\mathbf{x = 2\frac{2}{3}}$

(b) $5x - 3(x - 1) = 2$

$5x - 3x + 3 = 2$

$2x + 3 = 2$
$\quad (-3) \quad (-3)$

$2x = -1$
$(\div 2) \quad (\div 2)$

$\mathbf{x = -\frac{1}{2}}$

Example 4.4.2

Solve $\frac{3(x-1)}{4} - \frac{2(3x+1)}{3} = -1$

Solution

$$12 \times \left[\frac{3(x-1)}{4} - \frac{2(3x+1)}{3} \right] = 12 \times (-1)$$

$$9(x - 1) - 8(3x + 1) = -12$$
$$9x - 9 - 24x - 8 = -12$$
$$-15x - 17 = -12$$
$$(+17) \quad (+17)$$
$$-15x = 5$$
$$(\div -15) \ (\div -15)$$

$$x = \frac{5}{-15} = -\frac{1}{3}$$

Note: at Step 2 $\overset{3}{\cancel{12}} \times \frac{3}{\cancel{4}} = 9$ and $\overset{4}{\cancel{12}} \times \frac{2}{\cancel{3}} = 8$

Solving Linear Inequations

Inequations are solved using the same method as you use to solve an equation, i.e. by performing balancing operations to isolate the letter. However, there is a complication: if you multiply or divide both sides by a negative number, then you must switch the inequality sign round, i.e. change < to > or change > to <.

Here is an example using numbers:

$$-4 < -2 \quad \text{gives} \quad \frac{-4}{-2} > \frac{-2}{-2} \text{ i.e. } 2 > 1$$
$$(\div -2) \, (\div -2)$$

and an example with letters:

$$-3x < -2 \quad \text{gives} \quad \frac{-3x}{-3} > \frac{-2}{-3} \text{ i.e. } x > \frac{2}{3}$$
$$(\div -3) \, (\div -3)$$

Note: $a > x$ is rewritten $\quad x < a$
and $\quad a < x$ is rewritten $\quad x > a$

also $\quad -x < a$ is rewritten $\quad x > -a$
$\quad -x > a$ is rewritten $\quad x < -a$
$\quad -x < -a$ is rewritten $\quad x > a$
$\quad -x > -a$ is rewritten $\quad x < a$

In the last four examples, the result may be obtained by mutiplying both sides by −1.

Example 4.4.3

Solve $x + 6 \geq 5x + 10$

Solution

method 1 $\quad x + 6 \geq 5x + 10$
$\qquad\qquad (-x) \qquad\quad (-x)$

$$6 \geq 4x + 10$$
$$(-10) \qquad (-10)$$

$$-4 \geq 4x$$
$$(\div 4) \quad (\div 4)$$

$$-1 \geq x$$

rewrite as $\quad x \leq -1$

method 2 $\quad x + 6 \geq 5x + 10$
$\qquad\qquad (-5x) \qquad (-5x)$

$$-4x + 6 \geq 10$$
$$(-6) \quad (-6)$$

$$-4x \geq 4$$
$$(\div -4) \quad (\div -4)$$

switch the sign $x \leq \dfrac{4}{-4}$

$$x \leq -1$$

Note: $x \leq -1$ means all numbers **less than or equal to** −1 satisfy the original inequation.

Setting up a Linear Equation

Two adults and three children go to the cinema. Their tickets cost £13 in total. If the price of an adult and a child's ticket are not known then letters are used:
Child's ticket: £x $\qquad$ Adult's ticket: £y
Total cost is £$(3x + 2y)$

3 lots of £x $\qquad$ 2 lots of £y

So $3x + 2y = 13$ (a linear equation)

Example 4.4.4

The total cost of my journey one day was £15. The bus cost 30p per km and the taxi charged 50p per km. Set up a linear equation for this situation.

Solution
Distance travelled by bus: $\;b$ km
Distance travelled by taxi: $\;t$ km

Cost: $\quad 30b + 50t$ pence
$\qquad$ or $\;$ £$(0{\cdot}3b + 0{\cdot}5t)$
$\qquad$ so $\;0{\cdot}3b + 0{\cdot}5t = 15$

Solving Problems Algebraically

The general method is as follows:

step 1 Rearrange the equations (if necessary) to get the letters lined up.

step 2 Multiply the equations with the aim of matching the number of one of the letters in each equation.

step 3 Add or subtract to eliminate the matching letter then solve the resulting equation.

step 4 Put the value you found in Step 3 back into one of the original equations to find the value of the other letter.

Example 4.4.5

Solve $\quad \left. \begin{array}{l} 2x = 7 - 3y \\ 3x - 2y = 4 \end{array} \right\}$

Solution

step 1 Rearrange the 1st equation:
$$\left. \begin{array}{l} 2x + 3y = 7 \\ 3x - 2y = 4 \end{array} \right\}$$ *(x's and y's are now lined up)*

step 2 Let's match the x's:
$$\begin{array}{l} 2x + 3y = 7 \quad] \times 3 \\ 3x - 2y = 4 \quad] \times 2 \end{array}$$

This gives:
$$\left. \begin{array}{l} 6x + 9y = 21 \\ 6x - 4y = 8 \end{array} \right\}$$ *(The number of x's match in each equation)*

step 3
$$\begin{array}{l} 6x + 9y = 21 \\ 6x - 4y = 8 \end{array}$$
Subtract: $\quad 13y = 13$ *(Subtract −4 same as adding 4)*
$$\text{So } y = 1$$

step 4 Put $y = 1$ into $2x + 3y = 7$ giving
$$2x + 3 = 7$$
$$\text{so } 2x = 4$$
$$\text{so } x = 2$$

The solution is **x = 2** and **y = 1**

Example 4.4.6

A music station on the radio allows a fixed length of time for singles tracks and a longer fixed time for album tracks. One of the DJs knows that in his 35-minute program he can fit 3 album tracks and 5 singles tracks. He also knows that the time allocated for 7 singles tracks is 18 minutes more than the time allocated for 2 album tracks.

Tomorrow he is broadcasting a half-hour program and plans to play 3 album tracks and 4 singles tracks. Will he manage this?

Solution
The time allocated for 1 album track: a minutes
The time allocated for 1 singles track: s minutes

So $3a + 5s = 35$ (3 album tracks and 5 singles tracks in a 35-minute program)
Also $7s = 2a + 18$ (7 singles tracks are 18 minutes longer than 2 album tracks)

This gives:

step 1 $\left. \begin{array}{l} 5s + 3a = 35 \\ 7s - 2a = 18 \end{array} \right\}$

step 2 $\left. \begin{array}{l} 5s + 3a = 35 \\ 7s - 2a = 18 \end{array} \right\} \begin{array}{l} \times 2 \longrightarrow \\ \times 3 \longrightarrow \end{array} \left. \begin{array}{l} 10s + 6a = 70 \\ 21s - 6a = 54 \end{array} \right\}$

step 3 $\left. \begin{array}{l} 10s + 6a = 70 \\ 21s - 6a = 54 \end{array} \right\}$
Add: $31s = 124$
So $s = 4$

step 4 Put $s = 4$ in $5s + 3a = 35$
giving $20 + 3a = 35$ so $3a = 15$
so $a = 5$
album track: 5 minutes   singles track: 4 minutes

His plan needs $3a + 4s = 3 \times 5 + 4 \times 4 = 15 + 16 = 31$ minutes, 1 minute too long!

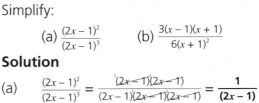
Cancelling Fractions

With Numbers	With Letters

$$\frac{10}{2} = \frac{\cancel{2} \times 5}{\cancel{2}} = \frac{5}{1} = 5 \qquad \frac{x(x+3)}{x} = \frac{\cancel{x} \times (x+3)}{\cancel{x}} = \frac{x+3}{1} = x+3$$

$$\frac{10}{14} = \frac{\cancel{2} \times 5}{\cancel{2} \times 7} = \frac{5}{7} \qquad \frac{(x-1)(x+2)}{(x-1)(x+5)} = \frac{\cancel{(x-1)} \times (x+2)}{\cancel{(x-1)} \times (x+5)} = \frac{x+2}{x+5}$$

$$\frac{7^2}{3 \times 7} = \frac{7 \times \cancel{7}}{3 \times \cancel{7}} = \frac{7}{3} \qquad \frac{(2x+1)^2}{3(2x+1)} = \frac{(2x+1) \times \cancel{(2x+1)}}{3 \times \cancel{(2x+1)}} = \frac{2x+1}{3}$$

Note

$\dfrac{a+b}{a}$ No cancelling allowed.

$\dfrac{a \times b}{a}$ Cancelling is allowed: $\dfrac{\cancel{a} \times b}{\cancel{a}} = \dfrac{b}{1} = b$

Example 4.5.1

Simplify:

(a) $\dfrac{(2x-1)^2}{(2x-1)^3}$ (b) $\dfrac{3(x-1)(x+1)}{6(x+1)^2}$

Solution

(a) $\dfrac{(2x-1)^2}{(2x-1)^3} = \dfrac{\cancel{(2x-1)}\cancel{(2x-1)}}{(2x-1)\cancel{(2x-1)}\cancel{(2x-1)}} = \dfrac{1}{(2x-1)}$

(b) $\dfrac{3(x-1)(x+1)}{6(x+1)^2} = \dfrac{\cancel{3}(x-1)\cancel{(x+1)}}{\cancel{6}(x+1)\cancel{(x+1)}} = \dfrac{(x-1)}{2(x+1)}$

With Numbers	With Letters

$\dfrac{45}{50}$ — Factorise / Factorise

factorise (difference of squares) $\dfrac{x^2 - y^2}{10x - 10y}$ ← factorise (common factors)

$= \dfrac{\cancel{5} \times 9}{\cancel{5} \times 10}$ Cancel the factor 5

$= \dfrac{9}{10}$

$= \dfrac{\cancel{(x-y)}(x+y)}{10\cancel{(x-y)}}$ cancel the factor $(x-y)$

$= \dfrac{x+y}{10}$

Example 4.5.2

Simplify:

(a) $\dfrac{2a^2 - 8b^2}{4a + 8b}$ (b) $\dfrac{x^2 - 7x + 12}{x^2 - 16}$

Solution

(a) $\dfrac{2a^2 - 8b^2}{4a + 8b} = \dfrac{2(a^2 - 4b^2)}{4(a + 2b)}$ ← Not fully factorised

$= \dfrac{\cancel{2}(a-2b)\cancel{(a+2b)}}{\cancel{4}\cancel{(a+2b)}}$ Cancel factors 2 and $(a+2b)$

$= \dfrac{a - 2b}{2}$

(b) $\dfrac{x^2 - 7x + 12}{x^2 - 16} = \dfrac{\cancel{(x-4)}(x-3)}{\cancel{(x-4)}(x+4)}$

$= \dfrac{(x-3)}{(x+4)}$

Multiplying Fractions

The basic rule is:

$$\frac{a}{b} \times \frac{c}{d} = \frac{ac}{bd}$$

← The two numerators are multiplied.
← The two denominators are multiplied.

Example 4.5.3

Simplify:

(a) $\dfrac{2x}{3} \times \dfrac{6y}{xy}$ (b) $\dfrac{3(x+1)^2}{5} \times \dfrac{1}{6(x+1)}$

Solution

(a) $\dfrac{2x}{3} \times \dfrac{6y}{xy}$ The cancelled factors are 3, x and y.

$= \dfrac{2 \times 2}{1 \times 1} = \dfrac{4}{1} = 4$

(b) $\dfrac{3(x+1)(x+1)}{5} \times \dfrac{1}{6(x+1)}$ The cancelled factors are 3 and $(x+1)$.

$= \dfrac{(x+1) \times 1}{5 \times 2} = \dfrac{x+1}{10}$

Cancelling of any factor found in both numerator and denominator can then take place.

It is often easier to do this cancelling before doing the multiplication:

With Numbers	With Letters

$\dfrac{7}{15} \times \dfrac{12}{49}$

$= \dfrac{\cancel{7}}{\cancel{15}} \times \dfrac{\cancel{12}}{\cancel{49}}$

$= \dfrac{1 \times 4}{5 \times 7} = \dfrac{4}{35}$

$\dfrac{x}{6} \times \dfrac{3(x+1)}{x^2}$

$= \dfrac{\cancel{x}}{\cancel{6}} \times \dfrac{\cancel{3}(x+1)}{x \times \cancel{x}}$

$= \dfrac{1 \times (x+1)}{2 \times x} = \dfrac{(x+1)}{2x}$

Dividing Fractions

Each division, for example $\frac{2a}{b} \div \frac{a^2}{b}$, can be written as a 'double-decker' fraction:

$\dfrac{\frac{2a}{b}}{\frac{a^2}{b}}$ The top and bottom of a fraction may be multiplied by the same number (or letter). In this case multiply top and bottom by b.

$$= \frac{\frac{2a}{b} \times b}{\frac{a^2}{b} \times b} = \frac{2a}{a^2} = \frac{2\cancel{a}}{a \times \cancel{a}} = \frac{2}{a}$$

This method copes with, for example, $\frac{3x}{4} \div 2$:

$\dfrac{\frac{3x}{4}}{2}$ Multiply top and bottom by 4 to get rid of the 4 in $\frac{3x}{4}$.

$$= \frac{\frac{3x}{4} \times 4}{2 \times 4} = \frac{3x}{8}$$

and also examples such as $8 \div \frac{a^2}{6}$:

$\dfrac{8}{\frac{a^2}{6}}$ Multiply top and bottom by 6 to get rid of the 6 in $\frac{a^2}{6}$.

$$= \frac{8 \times 6}{\frac{a^2}{6} \times 6} = \frac{48}{a^2}$$

Adding and Subtracting Fractions

Aim to get the two denominators equal:

With Numbers

$$\frac{2}{3} + \frac{1}{5}$$

$$= \frac{2 \times 5}{3 \times 5} + \frac{1 \times 3}{5 \times 3}$$

$$= \frac{10}{15} + \frac{3}{15} \quad \text{both '15th's}$$

$$= \frac{10 + 3}{15} = \frac{13}{15}$$

With Letters

$$\frac{2}{a} + \frac{1}{b}$$

$$= \frac{2 \times b}{a \times b} + \frac{1 \times a}{b \times a}$$

$$= \frac{2b}{ab} + \frac{a}{ab} \quad \text{both 'abth's}$$

$$= \frac{2b + a}{ab}$$

Example 4.5.4

Express each of these as a single fraction in its simplest form:

(a) $\dfrac{3a}{7(a + 1)} \div \dfrac{6}{(a + 1)^2}$ (b) $2x \div \dfrac{2}{3x}$

Solution

(a)
$$\frac{\dfrac{3a}{7(a+1)} \times 7\cancel{(a+1)}(a+1)}{\dfrac{6}{(a+1)(a+1)} \times 7(a+1)(a+1)}$$

$$= \frac{7a(a + 1)}{\cancel{42}^{14}} = \frac{a(a + 1)}{14}$$

(b)
$$\frac{2x \times 3x}{\dfrac{2}{3x} \times 3x}$$

$$= \frac{\cancel{6}^3 x^2}{2} = \frac{3x^2}{1} = \mathbf{3x^2}$$

Example 4.5.5

Express $\frac{2}{x^2} + \frac{1}{2x}$ as a single fraction.

Solution

$$\frac{2}{x^2} + \frac{1}{2x} \qquad \text{Aim: change both denominators to } 2x^2$$

$$= \frac{2 \times 2}{x^2 \times 2} + \frac{1 \times x}{2x \times x}$$

$$= \frac{4}{2x^2} + \frac{x}{2x^2} = \frac{\mathbf{4 + x}}{\mathbf{2x^2}}$$

Note 1

When making the two denominators the same look closely at the factors of each denominator:

for a and $3a^2$ make both $3a^2$

$(3 \times a \times a)$ $(3 \times a \times a)$

missing factor 3 and factor a so multiply by $3a$

for $2ab^2$ and $3a^2b$ change to $6a^2b^2$

$(2 \times a \times b \times b)$ $(3 \times a \times a \times b)$ $(2 \times 3 \times a \times a \times b \times b)$

missing factors   missing factors
3 and a so   2 and b so
multiply by $3a$ multiply by $2b$

Note 2

Always check your answer to see if cancelling is possible.

$$\frac{a+4}{3a} - \frac{1-2a}{3a} = \frac{a+4-(1-2a)}{3a}$$

$$= \frac{a+4-1+2a}{3a} = \frac{3a+3}{3a}$$ ——— Common factor of 3

$$= \frac{{}^1\cancel{3}(a+1)}{{}_1\cancel{3}a} = \frac{a+1}{a}$$

Changing the Subject of a Formula

At all times the aim is to isolate the required letter by treating both sides of the formula identically.

For example:

$$v = \sqrt{9-u^2}$$

square   square

$$v^2 = 9 - u^2$$

add u^2 add u^2

$$v^2 + u^2 = 9$$

subtract v^2 subtract v^2

$$u^2 = 9 - v^2$$

square root   square root

$$\mathbf{u} = \sqrt{9-v^2}$$

To change the subject to $\boldsymbol{u}$, get rid of the square root by doing the 'opposite', namely squaring.

It is easier without a minus sign in front of u^2 so do the 'opposite', namely add u^2.

Get rid of v^2 by subtracting it from both sides.

Finally get rid of squaring by doing the 'opposite', namely, square rooting.

$\boldsymbol{u}$ is now the subject of the formula

Example 4.5.6

Example 4.5.6

Express as a single fraction in its simplest form:

$$\frac{5}{x} - \frac{2}{x-3}$$

Solution

$$\frac{5}{x} - \frac{2}{x-3}$$ Change both denominators to $x(x-3)$.

$$= \frac{5 \times (x-3)}{x \times (x-3)} - \frac{2 \times x}{(x-3) \times x}$$

$$= \frac{5(x-3)}{x(x-3)} - \frac{2x}{x(x-3)}$$

$$= \frac{5(x-3) - 2x}{x(x-3)}$$ Now start to simplify.

$$= \frac{5x - 15 - 2x}{x(x-3)}$$

$$= \frac{3x - 15}{x(x-3)}$$

$$= \frac{3(x-5)}{x(x-3)}$$ (No cancelling possible!)

Example 4.5.7

Change the subject in the formulae:

(a) $r = \sqrt{\frac{A}{\pi}}$ to A   (b) $s = \frac{(u+v)t}{2}$ to t

Solution

(a) $r = \sqrt{\frac{A}{\pi}}$

square   square

$$r^2 = \frac{A}{\pi}$$

$\times \pi$ $\times \pi$

$$\pi r^2 = A$$

so $A = \pi r^2$ (Is this familiar?)

(b) $s = \frac{(u+v)t}{2}$

$\times 2$ $\times 2$

$$2s = (u+v)t$$

divide by $u+v$ divide by $u+v$

$$\frac{2s}{u+v} = t$$

so $t = \frac{2s}{u+v}$

Notes

In achieving your aim of isolating the required letter identify what you want rid of and do the opposite to each side.

For example:

You want rid of	Do this to both sides
$+2$	subtract 2
$\dfrac{\text{(something)}}{5}$	multiply by 5
$\sqrt{\text{something}}$	square
$(\text{something})^2$	square root

Simplifying Surds

For our purposes a surd is a square root of a number that on your calculator would give you an 'endless' decimal:

$\sqrt{2}$

1·4142135

This is a surd

$\sqrt{25}$

5

This is not a surd

When you are asked to 'simplify' a surd you have to make the number under the root sign as small as possible. How is this done?

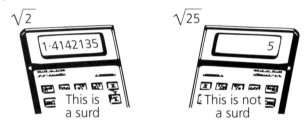

The key numbers are: 1   25   64   16   81   4   36   9   49   100   the square numbers.

For example:
$$\sqrt{108} = \sqrt{9 \times 12} = \sqrt{9} \times \sqrt{12} = 3 \times \sqrt{12}$$
However $\sqrt{12}$ can still be simplified:
$$3 \times \sqrt{12} = 3 \times \sqrt{4 \times 3} = 3 \times \sqrt{4} \times \sqrt{3}$$
$$= 3 \times 2 \times \sqrt{3} = 6 \times \sqrt{3}$$
Write this as $6\sqrt{3}$.
(Compare with $6 \times x$ written as $6x$.)
Alternatively:
$$\sqrt{108} = \sqrt{36 \times 3} = \sqrt{36} \times \sqrt{3} = 6 \times \sqrt{3} = 6\sqrt{3}$$

General rules are:
$$\sqrt{a \times b} = \sqrt{a} \times \sqrt{b}$$
and
$$\sqrt{\frac{a}{b}} = \frac{\sqrt{a}}{\sqrt{b}}$$

Example 4.6.1

Simplify:
 (a) $\sqrt{96}$ (b) $\sqrt{2} \times \sqrt{8}$
 (c) $\dfrac{\sqrt{6}}{\sqrt{2}}$ (d) $\sqrt{\dfrac{49}{100}}$

Solution

(a) $\sqrt{96} = \sqrt{16 \times 6} = \sqrt{16} \times \sqrt{6}$
$$= 4 \times \sqrt{6} = \mathbf{4\sqrt{6}}$$

(b) $\sqrt{2} \times \sqrt{8} = \sqrt{2 \times 8} = \sqrt{16} = \mathbf{4}$
(or $\sqrt{2} \times \sqrt{8} = \sqrt{2} \times \sqrt{2} \times \sqrt{4} = 2 \times 2 = \mathbf{4}$)

(c) $\dfrac{\sqrt{6}}{\sqrt{2}} = \sqrt{\dfrac{6}{2}} = \mathbf{\sqrt{3}}$

(or $\dfrac{\sqrt{6}}{\sqrt{2}} = \dfrac{\sqrt{2} \times \sqrt{3}}{\sqrt{2}} = \mathbf{\sqrt{3}}$)

(d) $\sqrt{\dfrac{49}{100}} = \dfrac{\sqrt{49}}{\sqrt{100}} = \dfrac{7}{10} = \mathbf{0{\cdot}7}$

Rationalising the Denominator

1. $\sqrt{a} \times \sqrt{a} = a$

You can use this fact to get rid of root signs on the denominators of fractions.
For example:

$$\frac{2}{\sqrt{3}} = \frac{2 \times \sqrt{3}}{\sqrt{3} \times \sqrt{3}} = \frac{2\sqrt{3}}{3} \quad \text{no root sign}$$

In general:

$$\frac{a}{\sqrt{b}} = \frac{a \times \sqrt{b}}{\sqrt{b} \times \sqrt{b}} = \frac{a\sqrt{b}}{b} \quad \text{no root sign}$$

2. $(a - \sqrt{b})(a + \sqrt{b})$

$$= a^2 + a\sqrt{b} - a\sqrt{b} - b = a^2 - b$$

You can use this fact to get rid of root signs in the denominators of fractions like this:

$$\frac{2}{4 - \sqrt{3}} = \frac{2 \times (4 + \sqrt{3})}{(4 - \sqrt{3}) \times (4 + \sqrt{3})}$$

$$= \frac{2(4 + \sqrt{3})}{16 + 4\sqrt{3} - 4\sqrt{3} - 3} = \frac{8 + 2\sqrt{3}}{13} \quad \text{no root sign}$$

Example 4.6.2

Express as a fraction with a rational denominator:

(a) $\dfrac{3}{\sqrt{6}}$ (b) $\dfrac{2}{\sqrt{18}}$ (c) $\dfrac{3}{5 + \sqrt{7}}$

Solution

(a) $\dfrac{3}{\sqrt{6}} = \dfrac{3 \times \sqrt{6}}{\sqrt{6} \times \sqrt{6}} = \dfrac{3\sqrt{6}}{6} = \dfrac{\sqrt{6}}{2}$

(b) $\dfrac{2}{\sqrt{18}} = \dfrac{2}{\sqrt{9 \times 2}} = \dfrac{2}{\sqrt{9} \times \sqrt{2}} = \dfrac{2}{3\sqrt{2}}$

$$= \dfrac{2 \times \sqrt{2}}{3\sqrt{2} \times \sqrt{2}} = \dfrac{2\sqrt{2}}{6} = \dfrac{\sqrt{2}}{3}$$

(c) $\dfrac{3}{5 + \sqrt{7}} = \dfrac{3 \times (5 - \sqrt{7})}{(5 + \sqrt{7}) \times (5 - \sqrt{7})}$

$$= \dfrac{3(5 - \sqrt{7})}{25 - 5\sqrt{7} + 5\sqrt{7} - 7} = \dfrac{3(5 - \sqrt{7})}{18}$$

$$= \dfrac{5 - \sqrt{7}}{6}$$

Working with Indices

Rule	Comments	Examples
$x^m \times x^n = x^{m+n}$	When multiplying, the indices are added. Note: not in the case $x^m \times y^n$!	$a^2 \times a^3 = a^{2+3} = a^5$
$\dfrac{x^m}{x^n} = x^{m-n}$	When dividing, the indices are subtracted.	$\dfrac{c^7}{c^3} = c^{7-3} = c^4$
$(x^m)^n = x^{mn}$	When raising a power to a power, multiply the indices.	$(y^3)^4 = y^{3 \times 4} = y^{12}$
$x^0 = 1$	Any number or expression (other than zero) raised to the power zero gives 1.	$2^0 = 1 \qquad (\frac{1}{2})^0 = 1$ $(a + b)^0 = 1$
$x^{-n} = \dfrac{1}{x^n}$	Something to a negative power can be rewritten as 1 divided by the same thing to the positive power.	$a^{-1} = \dfrac{1}{a^1} = \dfrac{1}{a} \quad a^{-3} = \dfrac{1}{a^3}$
$x^{\frac{m}{n}} = (\sqrt[n]{x})^m$	For a fractional power, the top number gives the power, and the bottom number gives the type of root. (2 means square root, 3 means cube root, etc...)	$a^{\frac{3}{2}} \quad a^{\frac{2}{3}}$ $= (\sqrt{a})^3 \quad = (\sqrt[3]{a})^2$

Example 4.6.3

Simplify: (a) $\dfrac{y^3 y^5}{y^2}$ (b) $5x^{-2} \times 2x$ (c) $a^{\frac{1}{2}} \times 4a^{-\frac{3}{2}}$ (d) $6a^2 \div 3a$ (e) $(m^{-\frac{3}{2}})^4$

Write your answer using positive indices where possible.

Solution   (a) $\dfrac{y^3 y^5}{y^2}$ *add these indices and subtract this index*

$= y^{3+5-2} = \boldsymbol{y^6}$

(b) $5x^{-2} \times 2x$
$= 5x^{-2} \times 2x^1$
$= 10x^{-2+1}$
$= 10x^{-1} = \dfrac{\boldsymbol{10}}{\boldsymbol{x}}$

(c) $a^{\frac{1}{2}} \times 4a^{-\frac{3}{2}}$
$= 4a^{\frac{1}{2}+(-\frac{3}{2})}$
$= 4a^{-1}$
$= \dfrac{\boldsymbol{4}}{\boldsymbol{a}}$

(d) $6a^2 \div 3a = \dfrac{\overset{2}{6}a^2}{\underset{1}{3}a}$

$= 2a^{2-1} = 2a^1 = \boldsymbol{2a}$

(e) $(m^{-\frac{3}{2}})^4 = m^{-\frac{3}{2} \times 4}$

$= m^{-6} = \dfrac{\boldsymbol{1}}{\boldsymbol{m^6}}$

Example 4.6.4

Change to index form ax^n: $\dfrac{1}{\sqrt{2x^3}}$

Solution $\dfrac{1}{\sqrt{2x^3}} = \dfrac{1}{\sqrt{2}\sqrt{x^3}} = \dfrac{1}{\sqrt{2}} \times \dfrac{1}{x^{\frac{3}{2}}} = \dfrac{\boldsymbol{1}}{\boldsymbol{\sqrt{2}}} \boldsymbol{x^{-\frac{3}{2}}}$

4.7 Solving Quadratic Equations

Quadratic Equations: Solutions by Factorising

The general method is as follows:

quadratic expression = 0

↓

(1st factor) × (2nd factor) = 0 ★

↓   ↓

1st factor = 0   or   2nd factor = 0

↓   ↓

Solve to get 1st solution   Solve to get 2nd solution

Note 1
At step ★ you use the fact that if you multiply two numbers to get zero then one or other of the two numbers is zero:

a × b = 0

↓   ↓

a = 0   or   b = 0

Note 2
A solution of an equation is called a **root** of the equation.

Example 4.7.1

Solve $x^2 - 2x - 3 = 0$

Solution

$$x^2 - 2x - 3 = 0$$
$$(x + 1)(x - 3) = 0$$

$x + 1 = 0$ or $x - 3 = 0$
$x = -1$ $x = 3$

The two roots of the equation are -1 and 3.

Example 4.7.2

Find the roots of the following quadratic equations:
(a) $3x^2 + 5x - 2 = 0$ (b) $3x^2 + 5x = 0$

Solution
(a) $3x^2 + 5x - 2 = 0$ (b) $3x^2 + 5x = 0$
     $(3x - 1)(x + 2) = 0$ $x(3x + 5) = 0$

$3x - 1 = 0$ or $x + 2 = 0$ $x = 0$ or $3x + 5 = 0$
   $3x = 1$ $x = -2$ $3x = -5$

   $x = \dfrac{1}{3}$ $x = -\dfrac{5}{3}$

The roots are $\dfrac{1}{3}$ and -2.   The roots are 0 and $-\dfrac{5}{3}$.

Quadratic Equations: Solutions by Formula

When solving $ax^2 + bx + c = 0$, sometimes $(\ ?\ )(\ ?\ ) = 0$ (the factorising step) does not work, i.e. the expression does not factorise.

In this case you use the **quadratic formula**:

$$ax^2 + bx + c = 0$$

$$x = \frac{-b + \sqrt{b^2 - 4ac}}{2a} \text{ or } x = \frac{-b - \sqrt{b^2 - 4ac}}{2a}$$

These are the two roots or solutions of the equation.

The compact way of writing this is $x = \dfrac{-b \pm \sqrt{b^2 - 4ac}}{2a}$

$\pm$ means there are two possibilities: one from adding, the other from subtracting.

Example 4.7.3

Solve $3x^2 - 4x - 2 = 0$ using an appropriate formula giving your answer correct to 1 decimal place.

Solution

$$3x^2 - 4x - 2 = 0$$
$$\text{compare} \quad ax^2 + bx + c = 0$$

This gives $\quad a = 3$ (the number of 'x^2's)
$\qquad\qquad b = -4$ (the number of 'x's)
and $\qquad c = -2$ (the constant term)

The appropriate formula is $x = \dfrac{-b \pm \sqrt{b^2 - 4ac}}{2a}$

which becomes: $x = \dfrac{-(-4) \pm \sqrt{(-4)^2 - 4 \times 3 \times (-2)}}{2 \times 3} = \dfrac{4 \pm \sqrt{16 + 24}}{6}$

$$= \frac{4 \pm \sqrt{40}}{6}$$

so $x = \dfrac{4 + \sqrt{40}}{6} \doteq \mathbf{1\cdot7}$ or $x = \dfrac{4 - \sqrt{40}}{6} \doteq \mathbf{-0\cdot4}$

$\qquad\qquad$ (to 1 d. p.) $\qquad\qquad\qquad$ (to 1 d. p.)

Note on Graphic Calculators

Graphic calculators are great for checking results. Usually a mistake in your calculation can be detected from a quick graph.

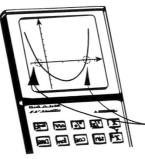

Graph: $y = 3x^2 - 4x - 2$
with Xmin: −1 Ymin: −5
$\qquad$ max: 2 $\qquad$ max: 5
$\qquad$ scl: 1 $\qquad$ scl: 1

These intersections seem reasonable for $x \doteq -0\cdot4$ and $x \doteq 1\cdot7$. You could 'zoom in' to check the results of your calculation more accurately.

Warning

Results written down directly from your graphic calculator will gain no marks. Full working is required. A graphic calculator is only useful for detecting possible errors in your calculation of the solution of an equation.

Variation: Direct, Inverse and Joint

Variation describes the way quantities are related. If quantity B is doubled or trebled, etc., and this causes quantity A to double or treble, etc, then A **varies directly** as B.

This may be written $A \propto B$. The relationship is $A = kB$, where k is a constant number called the constant of variation.

Similarly, if quantity B is doubled or trebled, etc, and this causes quantity A to be halved or thirded, etc, then A varies inversely as B. This may be written $A \propto \frac{1}{B}$.

The relationship is $A = k \times \frac{1}{B}$ or $A = \frac{k}{B}$ for some constant number k.

Various examples of different types of variation are given in this table:

Type	In words	In symbols	As an equation (k is the constant of variation)	As a graph	How to test for this type
Direct	y varies directly as x	$y \propto x$	$y = kx$	y is shown graphed against x	$\frac{y}{x}$ is constant (Divide the pairs of values to get the same value.)
Direct	y varies directly as the square of x	$y \propto x^2$	$y = kx^2$	y is shown graphed against values of x^2	$\frac{y}{x^2}$ is constant
Direct	y varies directly as the square root of x	$y \propto \sqrt{x}$	$y = k\sqrt{x}$	y is shown graphed against values of $\sqrt{x}$	$\frac{y}{\sqrt{x}}$ is constant
Inverse	y varies inversely as x	$y \propto \frac{1}{x}$	$y = \frac{k}{x}$	y is shown graphed against x	$y \times x$ is constant (Multiply the pairs of values to get the same value.)
Inverse	y varies inversely as the square of x	$y \propto \frac{1}{x^2}$	$y = \frac{k}{x^2}$	y is shown graphed against values of x^2	$y \times x^2$ is constant
Inverse	y varies inversely as the square root of x	$y \propto \frac{1}{\sqrt{x}}$	$y = \frac{k}{\sqrt{x}}$	y is shown graphed against values of $\sqrt{x}$	$y \times \sqrt{x}$ is constant
Joint (this combines several quantities)	y varies directly as x and inversely as z	$y \propto \frac{x}{z}$	$y = \frac{kx}{z}$		
Joint	y varies directly as the square of x and inversely as the square root of z	$y \propto \frac{x^2}{\sqrt{z}}$	$y = \frac{kx^2}{\sqrt{z}}$		

Note 1

If you are given values for the variables (letters) then the constant of variation, k, may be found by substituting these values into the equation and then solving it.

Note 2

The word 'direct' sometimes is left out: 'y varies as x' means 'y varies directly as x'. Similarly, 'y varies jointly as x and z' means 'y varies directly as x and directly as z'. This last example would result in the equation $y = kxz$.

Example 4.8.1

The time, T seconds, for a pendulum to swing varies directly as the square root of its length, L metres, and inversely as the square root of the 'strength' of gravity, g m/s².

On the surface of the Earth, g = 9·8 m/s² and a 1 metre pendulum has a swing of 2 seconds. How long, to the nearest second, would a swing of a 2 metre pendulum on the moon take, if g = 1·62 m/s² on the surface there?

Solution

$T \propto \frac{\sqrt{L}}{\sqrt{g}}$ so $T = \frac{k\sqrt{L}}{\sqrt{g}}$. You know T = 2 when g = 9·8 and L = 1.

So $2 = \frac{k \times \sqrt{1}}{\sqrt{9\cdot8}}$ giving $k = 2\sqrt{9\cdot8}$. The equation is $T = \frac{2\sqrt{9\cdot8}\sqrt{L}}{\sqrt{g}}$

When L = 2 and g = 1·62, then $T = \frac{2 \times \sqrt{9\cdot8} \times \sqrt{2}}{\sqrt{1\cdot62}} = 6\cdot956\ldots \div$ **7 seconds** (to the nearest second).

Variation: Changes to the Variable

Suppose $y \propto x$ and let's double x:
Since $y = kx$, then $k(2x) = 2kx = 2y$.
So doubling x has the effect of doubling y.

Suppose $y \propto x^2$: since $y = kx^2$, doubling x gives $k(2x)^2 = k \times 4x^2 = 4kx^2 = 4y$, and y has been multiplied by 4.

Suppose $y \propto \frac{1}{x}$: since $y = \frac{k}{x}$, doubling x gives $\frac{k}{2x} = \frac{1}{2} \times \frac{k}{x} = \frac{1}{2}y$, so y is halved.

Suppose $y \propto \frac{1}{x^2}$: this time let's treble x.

Since $y = \frac{k}{x^2}$, this gives us $\frac{k}{(3x)^2} = \frac{k}{9x^2} = \frac{1}{9} \times \frac{k}{x^2} = \frac{1}{9}y$, so that y has been divided by 9.

Example 4.8.2

The intensity, L units, of light on a screen varies inversely as the square of the distance, d metres, from the source of light. The screen is 2·5 metres from the light. If it is moved a further 7·5 metres away from the light, what is the effect on the intensity?

Solution

$L \propto \frac{1}{d^2}$ so $L = \frac{k}{d^2}$. The screen is now 10 m from the light, 4 times the original 2·5 m, and d has been multiplied by 4,

so $\frac{k}{(4d)^2} = \frac{k}{16d^2} = \frac{1}{16} \times \frac{k}{d^2} = \frac{1}{16}L$.

The intensity has been divided by 16 (reduced by a factor of 16).

What is Gradient?

Gradient is a number that measures the slope of a line. Divide the vertical distance by the horizontal distance:

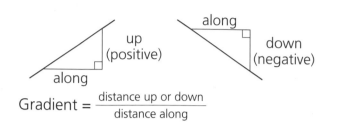

$$\text{Gradient} = \frac{\text{distance up or down}}{\text{distance along}}$$

Gradient Diagram

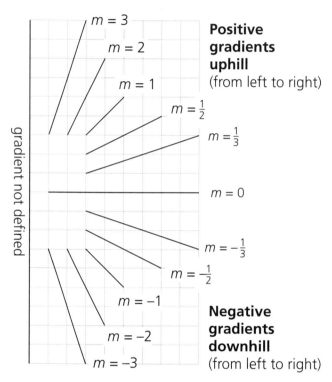

Positive gradients uphill (from left to right)

Negative gradients downhill (from left to right)

gradient not defined

Gradient Formula for Points

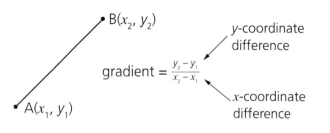

$$\text{gradient} = \frac{y_2 - y_1}{x_2 - x_1}$$

y-coordinate difference

x-coordinate difference

Note: $\frac{y_1 - y_2}{x_1 - x_2}$ gives the same result. So you can swap **both** top or bottom but not just one.

Example 5.1.1

Give the gradient of each line:

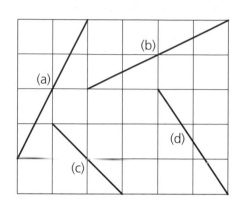

Solution

(a) 2 up, 1 along so gradient $= \frac{2}{1} =$ **2**

(b) 1 up, 2 along so gradient $= \frac{1}{2}$

(c) 1 down, 1 along so gradient $= \frac{-1}{1} =$ **−1**

(d) 3 down, 2 along so gradient $= \frac{-3}{2} = -\frac{3}{2}$

Example 5.1.2

Calculate the gradient of the line joining (−1, 3) and (2, −3).

Solution

$$\begin{aligned}
\text{gradient} &= \frac{3 - (-3)}{-1 - 2} \\
&= \frac{3 + 3}{-1 - 2} \\
&= \frac{6}{-3} \\
&= \textbf{−2}
\end{aligned}$$

Graphs from Equations

To draw the graph of a line from its equation there are two methods:

Method 1: Plot some points

step 1 Choose a few values for x and use the equation to calculate the corresponding values of y. It is helpful to put all the values in a table.

step 2 Draw a coordinate diagram. Since each pair of values in your table will be used as coordinates of a point, you can decide on a suitable scale for the two axes by looking at the table.

step 3 Plot the points on your diagram and draw a line through them.

Method 2: Use gradient and y-intercept

step 1 If necessary, rearrange the equation into the form: $y = ax + b$

step 2 Identify the gradient, a, and the y-intercept, $(0, b)$, where the line crosses the y-axis.

step 3 Use the information to sketch the graph. (The gradient diagram on page 46 may help.)

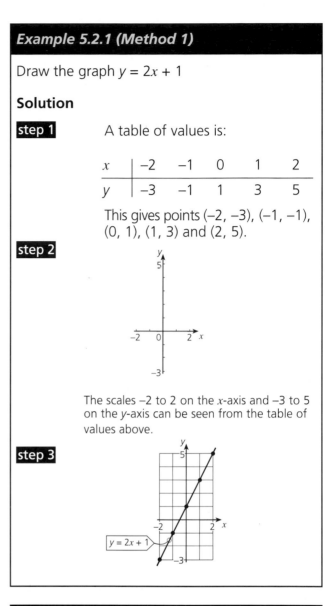

Example 5.2.1 (Method 1)

Draw the graph $y = 2x + 1$

Solution

step 1 A table of values is:

x	−2	−1	0	1	2
y	−3	−1	1	3	5

This gives points (−2, −3), (−1, −1), (0, 1), (1, 3) and (2, 5).

step 2

The scales −2 to 2 on the x-axis and −3 to 5 on the y-axis can be seen from the table of values above.

step 3

$y = 2x + 1$

Example 5.2.1 (Method 2)

Draw the graph $y - 2x = 1$

Solution

step 1 Add $2x$ to both sides to get:
$$y = 2x + 1$$

step 2 The gradient is 2. The y-intercept is (0, 1).

step 3

$y = 2x + 1$

Equations from Graphs

To find the equation of a line from its graph:

step 1 Calculate the gradient of the line. To do this you will need to draw a triangle on the grid with the sloping side along the line. Now use:

$$\text{Gradient} = \frac{\text{distance up or down}}{\text{distance along}}$$

step 2 Find the y-intercept: note the number on the y-axis where the line crosses.

step 3 The equation is:

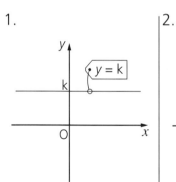

$y = \quad x + \quad$

The number from step 1 (gradient)

The number from step 2 (y-intercept)

Example 5.2.2

Find the equation of these lines:

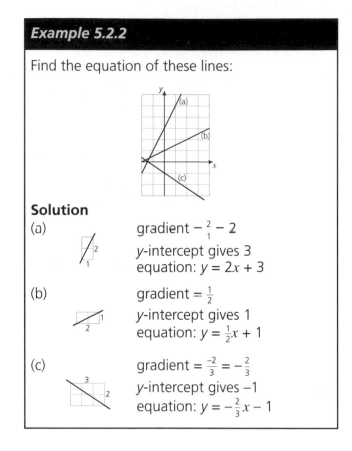

Solution

(a)
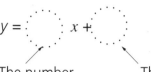
gradient $-\frac{2}{1} - 2$
y-intercept gives 3
equation: $y = 2x + 3$

(b)
gradient $= \frac{1}{2}$
y-intercept gives 1
equation: $y = \frac{1}{2}x + 1$

(c)
gradient $= \frac{-2}{3} = -\frac{2}{3}$
y-intercept gives -1
equation: $y = -\frac{2}{3}x - 1$

Special Lines

1.

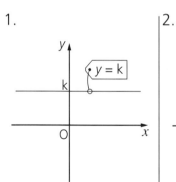

Equations of lines parallel to x-axis are of the form
y = 'a number'

2.

Equations of lines parallel to y-axis are of the form
x = 'a number'

3.

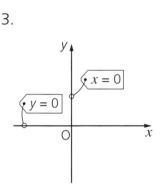

Equation of the x-axis is **$y = 0$**

Equation of the y-axis is **$x = 0$**

4.

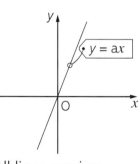

All lines passing through the origin (apart from the y-axis) have equations of the form **$y = ax$** where a is the gradient

---

What's the point?

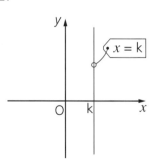

equation

(a, b)

The coordinates of points on the line satisfy the equation of the line.

The coordinates of points not on the line don't satisfy the equation of the line.

Example 5.2.3

Which of A $(-1, -5)$, B $(-3, 2)$ and C $(-2, 7)$ lies on the line $x + y = 5$?

Solution

For A: $x = -1$, $y = -5$ and $x + y = -1 + (-5) = -6$
For B: $x = -3$, $y = 2$ and $x + y = -3 + 2 = -1$
For C: $x = -2$, $y = 7$ and $x + y = -2 + 7 = 5$

Only **C** has coordinates that satisfy the equation so it lies on the line.

Parallel Lines

Lines which have the same gradient are parallel:

Other forms of equation for a line

$y + 4 = 3x$ $y = 1$

$2x = 3$

$2x - 3y = 2$

$x + 3y - 1 = 0$ $4 - 5x = y$

All these equations have an 'x-term' or a 'y-term' or both. The only other terms are numbers. These equations are all equations of straight lines.

Example 5.2.4

Are the lines $2y - 4x = 1$ and $y + 4 = 2x$ parallel?

Solution
$2y - 4x = 1$ (Add $4x$ to both sides.)
$2y = 4x + 1$ (Divide both sides by 2.)
$y = 2x + \frac{1}{2}$

     gradient is 2

$y + 4 = 2x$ (Subtract 4 from both sides.)
$y = 2x - 4$

     gradient is 2

The lines have the same gradient and are therefore **parallel**.

5.3 Solving Problems Graphically

Solving Problems Graphically: Simultaneous Equations

Three burgers and two pizzas cost £12.
Using letters: 1 burger costs £x
             1 pizza costs £y
Giving a total cost of £$(3x + 2y)$
So $3x + 2y = 12$
This linear equation can be graphed as shown in the diagram opposite.

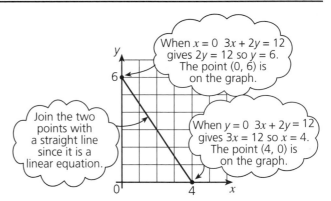

When $x = 0$ $3x + 2y = 12$ gives $2y = 12$ so $y = 6$. The point $(0, 6)$ is on the graph.

Join the two points with a straight line since it is a linear equation.

When $y = 0$ $3x + 2y = 12$ gives $3x = 12$ so $x = 4$. The point $(4, 0)$ is on the graph.

If you also know that one burger and one pizza together cost £5 then:
Using letters: $x + y = 5$
The graph of this linear equation can be added to the diagram as shown.

The two lines intersect at $(2, 3)$
giving $x = 2$ and $y = 3$ as the only pair of values for x and y that satisfy both equations simultaneously.
Thus a burger costs £2 and a pizza costs £3.
       $(x = 2)$ $(y = 3)$

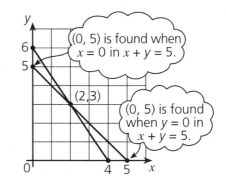

$(0, 5)$ is found when $x = 0$ in $x + y = 5$.

$(2, 3)$

$(0, 5)$ is found when $y = 0$ in $x + y = 5$.

Example 5.3.1

On the first day of my holiday I walked for 2 hours and cycled for 1 hour, covering 10 km that day. On my second day I walked for 1 hour and cycled for 2 hours, covering 14 km that day. I plan to walk 3 hours and cycle 3 hours on day three. How far will I cover?

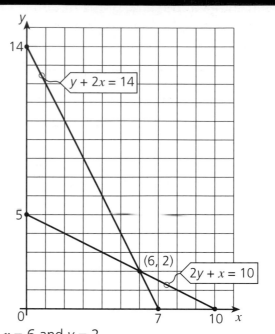

Solution

Cycling speed: x km/hr. Walking speed: y km/hr.

1st day: $2y$ + x =   10

   (2 hours at   (1 hour at   (10 km
     y km/hr) x km/hr)   covered)

2nd day: y + $2x$ =   14

   (1 hour at   (2 hours at   (14 km
    y km/hr) x km/hr)   covered)

From the graph the point of intersection is (6, 2) giving $x = 6$ and $y = 2$.
So I cycle at 6 km/hr and walk at 2km/hr.
On day 3: 3 hours cycling gives $3 \times 6 = 18$ km and 3 hours walking gives $3 \times 2 = 6$ km
i.e. $3x + 3y = 3 \times 6 + 3 \times 2 = 18 + 6 = 24$ km. I would expect to cover **24 km** on day 3.

Solving Problems Graphically: Iteration

To solve an equation $f(x) = 0$ by iteration you must consider the graph of $y = f(x)$

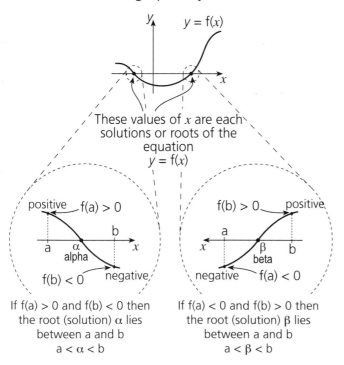

These values of x are each solutions or roots of the equation $y = f(x)$

If $f(a) > 0$ and $f(b) < 0$ then the root (solution) α lies between a and b
$a < \alpha < b$

If $f(a) < 0$ and $f(b) > 0$ then the root (solution) β lies between a and b
$a < \beta < b$

The example opposite shows how, by repeating calculations (iteration) a sign change (from positive to negative or negative to positive) can be used to 'home in' on the required root (solution) of the equation.

Example 5.3.2

The equation $x^3 + 3x^2 - 8 = 0$ has a root between 1 and 2. Use iteration to find the value of this root correct to 1 decimal place.

Solution: Let $f(x) = x^3 + 3x^2 - 8$ and let the required root be α (alpha):

$f(1) = 1^3 + 3 \times 1^2 - 8 = -4 < 0$
$f(2) = 2^3 + 3 \times 2^2 - 8 = 12 > 0$

so $1 < \alpha < 2$

Now do calculations to 1 decimal place:

$f(1\cdot1) = -3\cdot039 < 0$
$f(1\cdot2) = -1\cdot952 < 0$
$f(1\cdot3) = -0\cdot733 < 0$
$f(1\cdot4) = 0\cdot624 > 0$

so $1\cdot3 < \alpha < 1\cdot4$

Now do calculations to 2 decimal places to determine if α is nearer to $1\cdot3$ or $1\cdot4$. You need only try $x = 1\cdot35$.

$f(1\cdot3) = -0\cdot733 < 0$
$f(1\cdot35) = -0\cdot072\ldots < 0$
$f(1\cdot4) = 0\cdot624 > 0$

so $1\cdot35 < \alpha < 1\cdot4$
α is nearer to $1\cdot4$

The root is **1·4**, correct to 1 decimal place.

The Parabola

A graph showing the values of x^2 for all values of x can be built up from a few particular values:

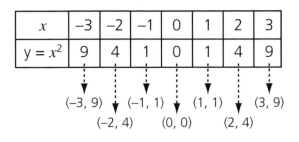

x	−3	−2	−1	0	1	2	3
$y = x^2$	9	4	1	0	1	4	9

(−3, 9) (−1, 1) (1, 1) (3, 9)
(−2, 4) (0, 0) (2, 4)

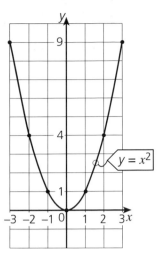

Notes

(1) This type of graph shape is called a **parabola**.
(2) The graph has symmetry, with the y-axis (the line $x = 0$) being the axis of symmetry.
(3) The graph has a minimum turning point at the origin (0, 0). This means that x^2 has a minimum value of 0 when $x = 0$.
(4) The equation $y = 0$ or $x^2 = 0$ has one **solution** (**root**), namely $x = 0$.

Quadratic Graphs

A quadratic graph has an equation of the form: $y = ax^2 + bx + c$ (where $a \neq 0$)

There must be an 'x^2 term' which can be positive or negative.

There may or may not be an 'x term'.

There may or may not be a 'constant term'.

The shape of this type of graph is always a parabola:

A positive 'x^2 term' gives:

a minimum turning point

A negative 'x^2 term' gives:

a maximum turning point

Example 5.4.1

The diagram shows the graph of $y = kx^2$. Use the information in the diagram to calculate the value of k.

(−1, 20)

$y = kx^2$

Solution

(−1, 20) lies on the graph $y = kx^2$ so $x = -1$ and $y = 20$ satisfy the equation giving:
$$20 = k \times (-1)^2$$
$$\text{so } 20 = k \times 1$$
$$\text{so } \mathbf{k = 20}$$

Quadratic Graphs: Solving Equations

To solve $ax^2 + bx + c = 0$ using a graph:

step 1 Construct a table of values of y for various values of x where
$$y = ax^2 + bx + c$$

step 2 Use the pairs of values (x, y) from step 1 to plot a series of points on a suitably scaled x-y axis diagram.

step 3 The solutions to $ax^2 + bx + c = 0$ are the values of x where the graph crosses the x-axis.

step 4 Check the solutions by substituting each value into $ax^2 + bx + c$. If your solution is correct it will give you a value of zero.

Note Unless asked to use a graph, you should always solve quadratic equations by factorising (see page 42) or by using the quadratic formula (see page 43).

Quadratic Graphs: Maximum/Minimum Values

From a quadratic graph that crosses the x-axis, you can find the maximum or minimum value on the graph as follows:

For a negative x^2-term:

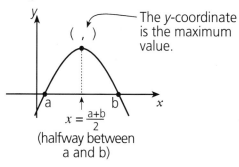

(halfway between a and b)

Similarly for a positive x^2-term:

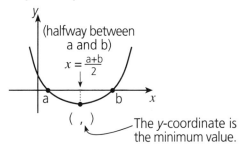

Use the 'halfway' x value in the graph formula to calculate the y-coordinate for max/min value.

Example 5.4.2

Solve $4x^2 - 8x - 5 = 0$ by drawing a suitable graph.

Solution

step 1 The table of values is:

x	−3	−2	−1	0	1	2	3
$y = 4x^2 - 8x - 5$	55	27	7	−5	−9	−5	7

step 2 The graph is:

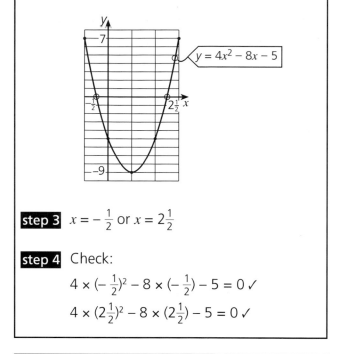

$y = 4x^2 - 8x - 5$

step 3 $x = -\frac{1}{2}$ or $x = 2\frac{1}{2}$

step 4 Check:
$$4 \times (-\tfrac{1}{2})^2 - 8 \times (-\tfrac{1}{2}) - 5 = 0 \checkmark$$
$$4 \times (2\tfrac{1}{2})^2 - 8 \times (2\tfrac{1}{2}) - 5 = 0 \checkmark$$

Example 5.4.3

It is known that the cross-sectional area, A cm², of this guttering is given by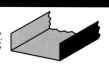

$$A(x) = 30x - 2x^2$$

Find the maximum value of this area.

Solution

The graph showing the values of the area will be a parabola. To find where it crosses the x-axis, you solve $A(x) = 0$

so
$$30x - 2x^2 = 0$$
$$2x(15 - x) = 0$$
$$x = 0 \quad \text{or} \quad x = 15$$

Here is a sketch of the graph:

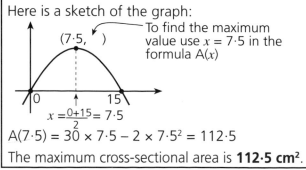

To find the maximum value use $x = 7.5$ in the formula $A(x)$

$$x = \frac{0+15}{2} = 7.5$$

$$A(7.5) = 30 \times 7.5 - 2 \times 7.5^2 = 112.5$$

The maximum cross-sectional area is **112·5 cm²**.

An Exponential graph

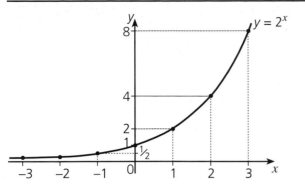

Points on the graph of $f(x) = 2^x$ are given by the following calculations:

$f(-3) = 2^{-3} = \frac{1}{2^3} = \frac{1}{8} \rightarrow (-3, \frac{1}{8})$

$f(-2) = 2^{-2} = \frac{1}{2^2} = \frac{1}{4} \rightarrow (-2, \frac{1}{4})$

$f(-1) = 2^{-1} = \frac{1}{2^1} = \frac{1}{2} \rightarrow (-1, \frac{1}{2})$

$f(0) = 2^0 = 1 \rightarrow (0, 1)$

$f(1) = 2^1 = 2 \rightarrow (1, 2)$

$f(2) = 2^2 = 4 \rightarrow (2, 4)$

$f(3) = 2^3 = 8 \rightarrow (3, 8)$

In general, exponential graphs have equations of the form $y = a^x$.

An Hyperbolic graph

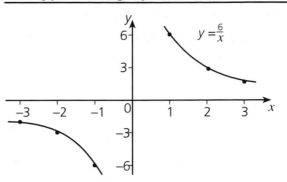

Points on the graph of $g(x) = \frac{6}{x}$ are given by the following calculations:

$g(-3) = \frac{6}{-3} = -2 \rightarrow (-3, -2)$

$g(-2) = \frac{6}{-2} = -3 \rightarrow (-2, -3)$

$g(-1) = \frac{6}{-1} = -6 \rightarrow (-1, -6)$

$g(0)$ is not defined (division by zero not on!)

$g(1) = \frac{6}{1} = 6 \rightarrow (1, 6)$

$g(2) = \frac{6}{2} = 3 \rightarrow (2, 3)$

$g(3) = \frac{6}{3} = 2 \rightarrow (3, 2)$

In general, hyperbolic graphs have equations of the form $y = \frac{a}{x}$.

Types of Graphs (reminders)

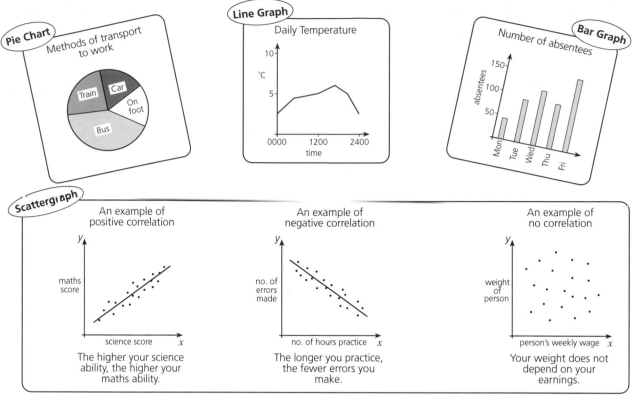

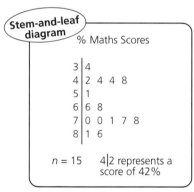

Stem-and-leaf diagram

% Maths Scores

```
3 | 4
4 | 2  4  4  8
5 | 1
6 | 6  8
7 | 0  0  1  7  8
8 | 1  6
```

$n = 15$ 4|2 represents a score of 42%

This type of diagram displays a graph of the data set using the actual numbers in the data set. It is a useful method of sorting the data into order when calculating the median and quartiles.

Data set: (% scores in a maths test)

70%, 44%, 42%, 78%, 48%, 44%, 70%, 34%, 81%, 51%, 68%, 86%, 66%, 71%, 77%

Pie Charts (an introduction)

In a **pie chart** all the data set is represented by a complete circle (the 'pie'). Each data value is represented by a sector of the circle (a 'slice of the pie').

The angle at the centre holds the key to all calculations concerning pie charts.

Since a complete circle requires 360° at the centre, the crucial fraction is: $\frac{\text{angle of sector}}{360}$
This gives the fraction of the data contained in that sector.

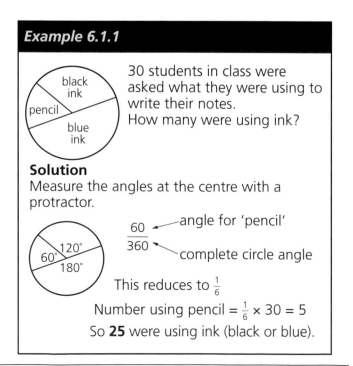

Example 6.1.1

30 students in class were asked what they were using to write their notes.
How many were using ink?

Solution
Measure the angles at the centre with a protractor.

$\frac{60}{360}$ — angle for 'pencil' / complete circle angle

This reduces to $\frac{1}{6}$

Number using pencil $= \frac{1}{6} \times 30 = 5$

So **25** were using ink (black or blue).

Constructing Pie Charts

step 1 Draw out a table showing each category of data along with its frequency.

step 2 Calculate the 'Circle Fraction' for each category.

step 3 Calculate the sector angle for each category using the 'Circle Fraction' of step 2 by calculating this fraction of 360°.

step 4 Use a protractor and the sector angles from Step 3 to construct the Pie Chart.

Note
Remember to add a title to your Pie Chart and also state what the full circle represents.

Example 6.1.2

30 commuters were asked the purpose of their journey. 13 said 'work', 12 were 'shopping', 3 'holiday' and 2 said 'visiting a friend'. Construct a pie chart to show this information.

Solution
Here is a frequency table:

Purpose	Frequency	Fraction	Sector Angle
Work	13	$\frac{13}{30}$	$\frac{13}{30} \times 360 = 156°$
Shopping	12	$\frac{12}{30}$	$\frac{12}{30} \times 360 = 144°$
Holiday	3	$\frac{3}{30}$	$\frac{3}{30} \times 360 = 36°$
Visiting	2	$\frac{2}{30}$	$\frac{2}{30} \times 360 = 24°$

Purpose of Journey

A full circle represents 30 commuters.

Cumulative Frequency

In a frequency table, it can be useful to keep a 'running total' of all the frequencies up to and including a given value.

Questions such as 'How many scored less than 45?' or 'How many were under 5 metres tall?' can then easily be answered using this **cumulative frequency column**.

Example 6.1.3

Five coins were thrown 20 times and the number of heads at each throw recorded:

2, 3, 2, 4, 2, 3, 1, 4, 2, 1,
4, 2, 0, 2, 3, 5, 3, 3, 2, 1.

(a) Construct a frequency table from this data and add a cumulative frequency column.

(b) In what % of throws were there 3 or fewer heads?

Solution

(a)

No of heads	Frequency	Cumulative Frequency
0	1	1
1	3	4
2	7	11
3	5	16
4	3	19
5	1	20

(b) 16 out of 20 throws gave 3 or fewer heads:
$\frac{16}{20} \times 100\% = $ **80%** of the throws.

Dotplots

Dotplots display each data value as a 'dot' above a numberline. This gives a useful indication of how the values in the data are distributed.

Example 6.1.4

A golfer records his scores over his last 15 games:

82,	91,	83,	82,	84,
78,	78,	85,	84,	77,
90,	85,	84,	85,	86.

Construct a dotplot from this data set and state his best score, worst score and middle score (median).

Solution

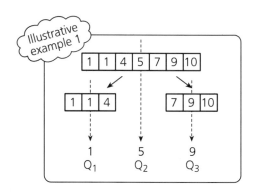

Golf scores

His best score was **77** and his worst was **91**. His median (middle) score was **84** (8th score in order).

Quartiles

If a data set is arranged in order (smallest to largest) and written as a list on a piece of tape, the tape can be cut into four equal pieces:

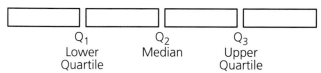

The values in the data set at the places where the tape is cut have names:

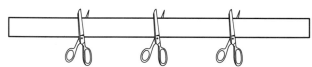

Q_1	Q_2	Q_3
Lower Quartile	Median	Upper Quartile

Sometimes there may be no value at the cut:

use 5   use $\frac{3+6}{2}$ = 4·5

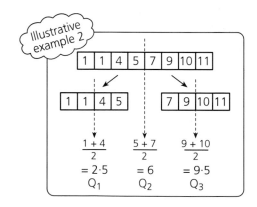

Example 6.1.5

A researcher counted the number of trips 17 marked bees made during the course of one day to collect nectar:

2,	3,	3,	1,	7,	2,
11,	12,	11,	6,	5,	11,
3,	7,	6,	8,	5.	

Calculate the Median and the Upper and Lower Quartiles for this data set.

Solution

The data in order gives:

1	2	2	3	3	3	5	5	6	6	7	7	8	11	11	11	12

1	2	2	3	3	3	5	5		6	7	7	8	11	11	11	12

The Median number of trips is **6**, the Upper Quartile is **9·5** and the Lower Quartile is **3**.

Boxplots

Boxplots are an effective way to illustrate the greatest and least values from a data set, along with its Median and Upper and Lower Quartiles:

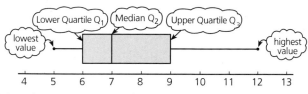

The 'box' stretches from Q_1 to Q_3 (6 to 9), with a line indicating the Median (7). 'Whiskers' extend to the lowest value (5) and to the highest value (12), indicating that the **range** is 7 (12 − 5 = 7).

Example 6.1.6

Construct a boxplot for this data set:
Midday temperatures (°C) for 2 weeks

| 3, | 8, | 9, | 7, | 7, | 5, | 11, |
| 12, | 12, | 12, | 13, | 9, | 7, | 7. |

Solution

Least: 3 Q_1: 7 Q_2: 8·5 Q_3: 12
Greatest: 13

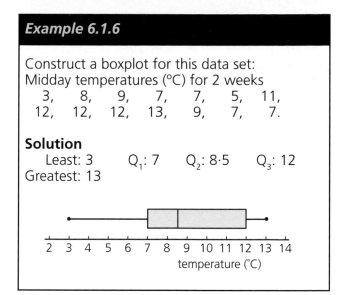

Scatter Graphs and Lines of Best Fit

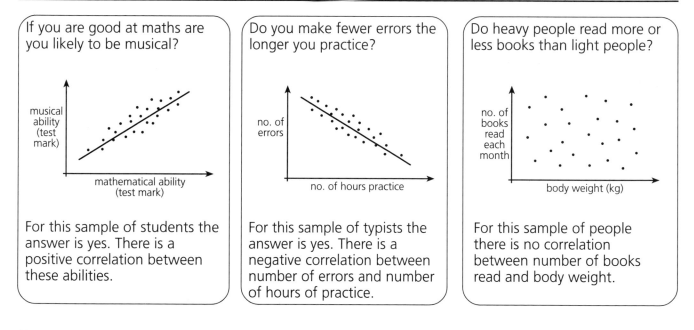

If you are good at maths are you likely to be musical?

For this sample of students the answer is yes. There is a positive correlation between these abilities.

Do you make fewer errors the longer you practice?

For this sample of typists the answer is yes. There is a negative correlation between number of errors and number of hours of practice.

Do heavy people read more or less books than light people?

For this sample of people there is no correlation between number of books read and body weight.

Note

Where there is positive or negative correlation, we can draw a straight line that approximately fits the points. This is called the line of best fit.

Example 6.1.7

A sample of six fathers and their grown-up sons were weighed. The results are given in the table:

Father's weight (kg)	62	67	70	71	68	64
Son's weight (kg)	63	66	67	68	66	63

(a) Draw a scattergraph for this data and describe the type of correlation involved.
(b) Draw a 'line of best fit', find its equation and use this to predict the weight of a man whose father weighed 75 kg.

Solution

(a)

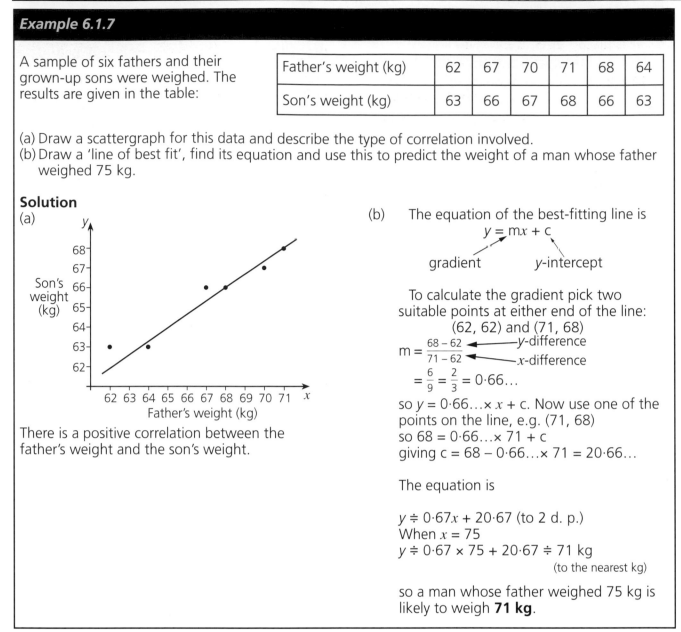

There is a positive correlation between the father's weight and the son's weight.

(b)   The equation of the best-fitting line is
$$y = mx + c$$
        gradient y-intercept

To calculate the gradient pick two suitable points at either end of the line:
(62, 62) and (71, 68)

$m = \dfrac{68 - 62}{71 - 62}$ ←—— y-difference
←—— x-difference

$= \dfrac{6}{9} = \dfrac{2}{3} = 0.66\ldots$

so $y = 0.66\ldots \times x + c$. Now use one of the points on the line, e.g. (71, 68)
so $68 = 0.66\ldots \times 71 + c$
giving $c = 68 - 0.66\ldots \times 71 = 20.66\ldots$

The equation is

$y \doteq 0.67x + 20.67$ (to 2 d. p.)
When $x = 75$
$y \doteq 0.67 \times 75 + 20.67 \doteq 71$ kg
(to the nearest kg)

so a man whose father weighed 75 kg is likely to weigh **71 kg**.

Averages and the Range (reminders)

For the data set: 2, 3, 1, 3, 1, 8

The Mean

Mean $= \dfrac{2+3+1+3+1+8}{6}$ ⟵ (total of values)

⟵ (number of values)

$= \dfrac{18}{6} = 3$

Mean $= \dfrac{\text{total of values}}{\text{number of values}}$

The Median

1   1   2 | 3   3   8

Median $= \dfrac{2+3}{2} = 2{\cdot}5$

The median is the middle value once the data set is ordered (smallest to largest) or the mean of the two middle values.

The Mode

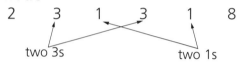

2   3   1   3   1   8

two 3s   two 1s

There are two modes: 1 and 3.
The mode is the most frequent value or values.

The Range

2   3   1   3   1   8

least value   greatest
is 1   value is 8

Range $= 8 - 1 = 7$
Range $=$ greatest value – least value

Quartiles and the Semi-interquartile Range

Remember the quartiles Q_1, Q_2 and Q_3 split the ordered data set into four equal sets of data:
The semi-interquartile range is given by:

	Q_1	Q_2	Q_3

$\frac{1}{2}(Q_3 - Q_1)$

and gives a measure of the distribution of the data. 'Clumped' data will give a relatively small number and 'spread out' data will give a relatively large number.

Example 6.2.1

Calculate the Range, Mean, Median and Mode for the data shown in the following frequency table which shows the number of errors made by 30 typists in a typing test.

Number of Errors	0	1	2	3	4	5	6
Frequency	10	7	4	2	4	1	2

Solutions
Add two columns to the frequency table:

No of errors	Frequency	Cumulative Frequency	No of errors × frequency
0	10	10	0 × 10 = 0
1	7	17	1 × 7 = 7
2	4	21	2 × 4 = 8
3	2	23	3 × 2 = 6
4	4	27	4 × 4 = 16
5	1	28	5 × 1 = 5
6	2	30	6 × 2 = 12

Total = 30   Total no. of errors = 54

Greatest no. of errors is 6 and the least is 0.
So Range $= 6 - 0 =$ **6 errors**.

The Mode (most frequent) is **0 errors**.

The Mean $= \dfrac{54}{30}$ ⟵ (Total no. of errors)

⟵ (no. of typists)

$=$ **1·8 errors**

The Median (middle value) is the Mean of the 15th and 16th no. of errors when they are listed in increasing order, i.e. $\dfrac{1+1}{2} =$ **1 error**.

Example 6.2.2

10 girls and 10 boys were chosen at random in a school and given a test consisting of 30 subtractions. The number of errors made was recorded:

Girls: 6, 3, 0, 5, 5, 4, 0, 4, 5, 4
Boys: 9, 3, 2, 10, 6, 5, 2, 1, 7, 2

Calculate the median and the semi-interquartile range for each of these data sets and comment on the results.

Standard Deviation

Standard Deviation is a measure of the distribution of a data set. It gives a measure of how 'spread out' the values are around their Mean value.

The formula we will use here is:

$$s = \sqrt{\frac{\Sigma(x - \bar{x})^2}{n - 1}}$$

This calculates the Standard Deviation, s, for a sample of values taken from a larger population. Here are the steps required to use this formula:

step 1 Calculate the Mean, $\bar{x}$, of the values:

$$\bar{x} = \frac{\text{sum of values}}{\text{number of values}} = \frac{\Sigma x}{n}$$

step 2 Calculate the deviation of each value from the Mean:

value – Mean = $x - \bar{x}$.

step 3 Square each deviation:

(value – Mean)^2 = $(x - \bar{x})^2$

step 4 Calculate the sum of these squared deviations:

Sum of squared deviations = $\Sigma(x - \bar{x})^2$

Example 6.2.2 (cont.)

Solution
The ordered data sets are:
Girls: 0 0 3 4 4 | 4 5 5 5 6

$$\underset{Q_1}{3} \qquad \underset{Q_2}{\overset{\frac{4+4}{2}}{= 4}} \qquad \underset{Q_3}{5}$$

Boys: 1 2 2 2 3 | 5 6 7 9 10

$$\underset{Q_1}{2} \qquad \underset{Q_2}{\overset{\frac{3+5}{2}}{= 4}} \qquad \underset{Q_3}{7}$$

Semi-interquartile Ranges are:

$$\text{Girls} = \tfrac{1}{2}(Q_3 - Q_1) = \tfrac{1}{2}(5 - 3) = 1$$

$$\text{Boys} = \tfrac{1}{2}(Q_3 - Q_1) = \tfrac{1}{2}(7 - 2) = 2 \cdot 5$$

Although the Median number of errors is the same, 4, for both boys and girls there is much more variation in the number of errors made by boys as indicated by the larger semi-interquartile range for the boys (2·5) compared to that for the girls (1).

Example 6.2.3

A Quality Control Inspector selects a random sample of six matchboxes produced by a machine and records the number of matches in each:

52   46   50   51   49   52

Calculate the Mean and Standard Deviation for this sample.

Solution:

step 1 Mean $\bar{x} = \frac{52 + 46 + 50 + 51 + 49 + 52}{6} = \frac{300}{6} = 50$

step 2 The deviations from the Mean are:
2, –4, 0, 1, –1, 2

step 3 The squared deviations are:
4, 16, 0, 1, 1, 4

step 4 Sum of the squared deviations:
4 + 16 + 0 + 1 + 1 + 4 = 26

step 5 The Standard Deviation is given by

$$s = \sqrt{\frac{26 \;\longleftarrow\; \text{sum of squared deviations}}{5 \;\longleftarrow\; \text{there were 6 values}}}$$

$$= \sqrt{5 \cdot 2} = \mathbf{2 \cdot 3} \text{ (to 1 d.p.)}$$

The Mean number of matches in a box is 50 and the Standard Deviation is 2·3 matches. (Usually around 95% of values are within 2 standard deviations of the Mean. In this case most boxes the machine produces will contain between 45 and 55 matches.)

step 5 Divide the answer in Step 4 by one less than the number of values, then take the square root. This gives the Standard Deviation:

$$s = \sqrt{\frac{\text{sum of squared deviations}}{\text{number of values} - 1}} = \sqrt{\frac{\Sigma(x - \bar{x})^2}{n - 1}}$$

(The formula $s = \sqrt{\frac{\Sigma(x - \bar{x})^2}{n - 1}}$ used above is one of two formulae given to you in the exam.

The other is: $s = \sqrt{\frac{\Sigma x^2 - \frac{(\Sigma x)^2}{n}}{n - 1}}$ and will give the same result.)

Advice

It is best to use a table layout for all the calculations involved in using this formula. The example opposite shows how this may be done.

Note

Scientific and Graphic Calculators have a Statistics or STAT mode. In this mode data sets may be keyed in and various statistics calculated.

For example, after entering the data set:

$\boxed{n}$ gives the number of data values;

$\boxed{\Sigma x}$ gives the total of the data values;

$\boxed{\bar{x}}$ gives the mean;

$\boxed{\sigma_{n-1}}$ gives the sample Standard Deviation.

You should consult your calculator manual to find out how to use these facilities.

Example 6.2.3 (cont.)

In table form:

x Number of matches	$x - \bar{x}$ Deviations from Mean	$(x - \bar{x})^2$ Squared deviations
52	2	4
46	−4	16
50	0	0
51	1	1
49	−1	1
52	2	4
$\Sigma x = 300$		$\Sigma(x - \bar{x})^2 = 26$

$\bar{x} = \frac{300}{6} = 50 \qquad \frac{\Sigma(x - \bar{x})^2}{n - 1} = \frac{26}{5} = 5 \cdot 2$

so s (Standard Deviation) = $\sqrt{5 \cdot 2}$ = **2·3** (to 1 d.p.)

Probability

The probability of an event happening is a number from 0 to 1:

The event will not happen.

The event is just as likely to happen as not to happen.

The event is certain to happen.

In some cases your knowledge of a situation will allow you to calculate the probability of an event happening:

$$\text{Probability of an event} = \frac{\text{no. of outcomes that make the event happen}}{\text{total no. of possible outcomes in the situation}}$$

For example if the event is: 'rolling an odd prime with a dice' then two outcomes 3 and 5 allow the event to happen. In this situation there are 6 possible outcomes (rolling 1 up to 6).

Probability of rolling an odd prime

$= P(\text{odd prime}) = \dfrac{2}{6}$ ← favourable outcomes ← possible outcomes

$= \dfrac{1}{3}$

Note 1

If p is the probability of an event happening then $(1 - p)$ is the probability of the event **not** happening. In the example of rolling an odd prime $1 - \frac{1}{3} = \frac{2}{3}$ is the probability of not rolling an odd prime.

Note 2

Probabilities can also be estimated from a sample data set as in the example opposite.

Example 6.3.1

Which is more likely: drawing a face card from a pack of cards or rolling a six with a dice?

Solution

Each of the 4 suits has 3 face cards (J, Q and K) so there are 12 face cards out of 52 cards:

$$\text{Probability of drawing a face card} = \frac{12}{52} \doteqdot 0{\cdot}23 \text{ (to 2 d.p.)}$$

Rolling a six can happen in 1 way out of 6 possible outcomes:

Probability of rolling a six $= \frac{1}{6} \doteqdot 0{\cdot}17$ (to 2 d.p.)

Drawing a face card has a higher probability and so is more likely.

Example 6.3.2

A random sample of 50 school students were asked the number of children in their families (including themselves). The results were:

No. of children in family	1	2	3	4	5	6
No. of students	8	24	16	1	0	1

Estimate the probability of a randomly picked student having only 1 brother or sister. How many such students would you expect at the school if the total roll is 1000 students?

Solution

P(family size 2) $= \frac{24}{50} = 0{\cdot}48$

Expected no. at school $= 0{\cdot}48 \times 1000$
$= \mathbf{480}$

Index